The Detox Way

Everyday Recipes to Feel Energized, Focused, and Physically and Mentally Empowered

Nour Zibdeh, MS RDN CLT

Nourition, LLC
www.NourZibdeh.com
support@nourzibdeh.com

ISBN: 978-0-9984371-0-1
Interior design: Weller Smith Design

Special Thank you

To my mom who believed there was a special book in me
and insisted that I go for it!

To my husband who took so much off my plate so I can dedicate
time and energy to this book.

To my kids who gave me the thumbs up—most of the time.

To my readers and patients who asked questions and shared
their struggles and success stories that inspired me to
create these delicious recipes.

To my friend and neighbor who offered her photography skills

To Maite, Diana, LeAnna, and Barbara for all your help
along putting this book together.

And to my family and friends who cheered me and supported
me along the way.

And to you, my dear reader, for supporting this book and
believing in me.

To express my gratitude, I have one more bonus for
you. A 7-day meal plan with shopping list and prepare
ahead instructions. Visit
www.nourzibdeh.com/TDWBonus
and get it.

Thank You.

About the Author

Nour Zibdeh, MS RDN CLT, is a registered dietitian and functional nutritionist. She uses functional nutrition therapies, including detoxification, to help her patients improve their health and live fulfilling lives. She helped hundreds of people lose weight, overcome digestive problems through healing the gut, uncover and overcome food sensitivities, manage diabetes and heart disease, manage auto-immune conditions through food and proper supplements, improve thyroid and adrenal function, and eliminate chronic fatigue. Nour is based in Northern Virginia where she sees patients in her practice. She also consults with individuals virtually.

Nour is a wife and mom of three active boys. She understands the daily struggles of making clean wholesome meals! In her book, she shares the recipes she makes for her family and friends and the recipes she recommends to her patients. Flavor and wholesomeness are non-negotiable in her food dictionary.

Nour believes that everyone has a goal and mission in life. Healing, nourishing, and clean foods are the foundation of a body and mind that are energized, focused, and empowered to fulfill these goals. She is passionate to contribute to your mission by taking the stress of what to eat away, setting you free to pursue your goals and dreams.

Connect with Nour:

Website: https://www.nourzibdeh.com

Facebook: https://www.facebook.com/nourition

YouTube: https://www.youtube.com/NourZibdeh

Pinterest: https://www.pinterest.com/nourzibdeh/

Instagram: https://www.instagram.com/nourzibdehnutrition/

Table of Contents

ABOUT THE AUTHOR 4

INTRODUCTION 9

Section 1: Learn 13

BALANCE YOUR MEALS 14

What Balance Means and
Why it Matters | 14

Vegetables | 17

Proteins | 20

Carbohydrates | 28

Fats | 32

Losing weight | 37

Water | 40

BALANCE CHEAT SHEETS 43

Non-starchy Vegetables | 44

Healthy Carbohydrates | 45

Understanding Carbohydrates
Numbers in Labels | 46

Healthy Proteins | 47

Healthy Fats | 48

Best Oils for Cooking and Salads | 49

Healthy Salad Builder | 50

Healthy Smoothie Builder | 51

Healthy Snack Builder | 52

Healthy Snack List | 53

DETOX WITH FOOD 54

What Detox Means and Why It Matters | 54

Top 12 Foods For Detox | 56

Gluten and Dairy | 62

REFERENCES 65

Section 2: Cook 67

Recommended Tools | 68

Measurement Conversions | 69

Healthy Pantry, Fridge, and Freezer List | 69

BASIC RECIPES 71

Chicken Stock with Chicken Meat | 72

Chicken Stock (without Chicken Meat) | 73

Shredded Chicken Breast | 74

Bone Broth | 75

Hard-Boiled Eggs | 76

Basic Salad Dressing | 77

Steamed Vegetables | 78

Zucchini Noodles | 79

Dry Beans on the Stovetop | 80

Dry Beans in the Slow Cooker | 81

Everyday Lentils | 82

Everyday Quinoa | 83

Everyday Rice | 84

Everyday Baked Potato or Sweet Potato | 85

BREAKFAST RECIPES 87

Everyday Vegetable Omelet | 88

Poached Eggs | 89

Mixed Vegetable Frittata | 90

Egg Avocado Salad | 92

Black Bean Egg Bake | 93

Whole Chia Seed Pudding | 92

Nutty Fruit Breakfast | 94

Everyday Oatmeal | 95

Muesli | 96

Sweet Potato Pancakes | 97

LUNCHES AND DINNERS 99
Side Soups 101

Basic Vegetable Soup | 102

Middle Eastern Pureed Red
Lentil Soup | 103

Chunky Brown Lentil Soup | 104

Curried Butternut Squash Soup | 105

Tomato Clam Chowder | 106

Side Salads 107

Chopped Kale Salad
with Almond Vinaigrette | 108

Arugula and Fennel Salad
with Orange Vinaigrette | 109

Detox Cauliflower Salad | 110

Chickpea Mango Fusion Salad | 111

Avocado Salad | 112

Peach and Black Bean Salad | 113

Middle Eastern Parsley Salad
With Tahini Dressing | 114

Roasted Eggplant Salad | 115

Beet and Carrot Salad | 116

Main Dish Soups and Stews 117

Hearty Chicken Vegetable Stew | 118

Tex-Mex Chicken Soup | 119

Turkey Chili | 120

Middle Eastern Lamb Stew
with Green Beans | 121

Main Dish Salads 123

Asian Chicken Cole Slaw | 124

Grilled Scallop Citrus Salad | 125

Tuna Avocado Salad | 126

Pomegranate Tuna Salad | 127

Shrimp Detox Salad | 128

Beef Taco Salad | 129

Vegetable Dishes 131

Eggplant and Zucchini Ratatouille | 132

Roasted Peppers And Mushrooms | 133

Sautéed Colorful Cabbage | 134

Roasted Brussels Sprouts | 135

Mashed Cauliflower | 136

Sautéed Collard Greens | 137

Vegetable Stuffed Portobello
Mushrooms | 138

Roasted Asparagus | 139

Roasted Turmeric Cauliflower | 140

Grilled Zucchini | 141

Protein Dishes 143

Five Herb Chicken | 144

Chicken with Herbed Tomatoes and
Mushrooms | 145

Grilled Chicken Kebabs | 146

Yellow Chicken with
Avocado Dressing | 147

Coconut Chicken Nuggets
with Spicy Honey Mustard Sauce | 148

Basic Broiled Salmon | 149

Zesty Herbed Salmon | 150

Pan-Seared Scallops | 151

Lemon Garlic Scampi | 152

Pecan Crusted Flounder | 153

Tomato Olive Baked Cod | 154

Carbohydrates Dishes 155

Roasted Spaghetti Squash | 156

Creamy Red Potato Salad | 157

Herb Red Potatoes | 158

Quinoa Vegetable Pilaf | 159

3-in-1 Meals 161

Beef Vegetable Stir-Fry | 162

Chicken and Greens over
Sweet Potatoes | 163

Detox Sheppard's Pie | 164

Salmon with Collard Greens
and Beans | 165

Baked Chicken Fajita | 166

Thai Chicken Wraps with
Almond Sauce | 167

Salmon with Mango Rice | 168

Sirloin Steak with Beans and
Basil Sauce | 169

Pot Roast with Vegetables | 170

Cauliflower Fried Rice
with Shrimp | 171

Veggie Lovers Sphaghetti Sauce | 172

SMOOTHIES 173

Kale Pineapple Smoothie | 174

Avocado Spinach Smoothie | 175

Banana Peach Smoothie | 176

Creamy Strawberry Smoothie | 177

Purple Smoothie | 178

Cilantro Citrus Smoothie | 179

SMALL BITES 181
Savory Bites 183

Homemade Chunky Salsa | 184

Chunky or Smooth Guacamole | 185

Middle Eastern Eggplant Dip
(baba ghanoush) | 186

Hummus Dip | 187

Olive Tapenade | 188

Lentil Eggplant Bowl | 189

Nori Wraps | 190

Roasted Chili Chickpeas | 191

Lemon Herb Chickpeas | 192

Sweet Bites 193

Date Chia Muffins | 194

Coconut Chocolate Chip Muffins | 195

Banana Almond Muffins | 196

Zucchini Bread | 197

Date Bars | 198

INDEX 200

Introduction

Congratulations! You have a complete resource that helps eliminate the stress of what to eat. Now you can make meals that energize you, improve your focus, supply you with mental and physical strength, enhance your mood, and help you lose weight.

The Detox Way cookbook has two main themes, detox and balance. All the recipes are made with detox-supporting ingredients in amounts that result in balanced meals..

Detox sounds like a crazy trend or fad but it's not. Your liver is constantly detoxing. Overtime, your body accumulates toxins from food such as residues from pesticides and herbicides, rancid and processed oils, charred foods, preservatives, food colorings, artificial sweeteners, and synthetic ingredients. Toxic compounds from water, plastics, bisphenols (like BPA and others), organic pollutants, car fumes, smoke, alcohol, prescription or over-the-counter medications, cleaning products, make-up and personal care products, and chemicals from house renovation projects, hobbies (ex. painting), or worksites (ex. hair salons or construction) increase your liver's detoxification load.

Some of us are better at detoxing than others. Your genetic make-up contributes 15% of how well you clear waste. Diet and lifestyle contribute 85%! That's a crazy lot! And that means you CAN and HAVE to be conscious about your choices.

If you have 2 or more of these complaints, then a bottleneck in your detoxification system may be to blame:
- Sluggish, tired, fatigued
- Brain fog, difficulty focusing
- Depression
- Restless or hyperactive
- Anxiety, irritability, mood swings
- Insomnia, trouble falling back to sleep
- Weight gain or difficulty losing weight
- Muscle and joint aches
- Fibromyalgia
- Headaches
- Skin issues like eczema, acne, psoriasis
- Dependent on sweets, carbs, and/or coffee for energy
- Intense sugar and other cravings
- Bloating and water retention
- Post nasal drip, frequent need to clear throat

What you choose to eat affects your how you feel. Detox-boosting foods help your body kick toxins out so the person hiding behind these symptoms can thrive.

The second theme of the book is balancing meals to help balance sugar and cravings. You can eat detox vegetables and fruits all day and still have cravings and energy crashes. The recipes are designed to contain the right amount of vegetables, proteins, fats, and carbohydrates so they are more satisfying. And when you feel satisfied, you graze less, have fewer cravings, and you will start losing weight without even trying.

There's no shortage of recipes or cookbooks out there, but even 'clean' recipes and cookbooks have some problems:

Some books claim to be 'clean' but use ingredients that are inflammatory. Refined vegetable oils, processed meats, artificial sweeteners, processed spreads and condiments, butter substitutes do not fit in a clean way of eating. The recipes in *The Detox Way* are made with the freshest most wholesome anti-inflammatory ingredients.

Many clean eating books are bland. *The Detox Way* recipes use a lot of herbs and spices that stimulate your senses. You won't believe healthy food can taste that good! Imagine how easy it would be to make healthy eating a lifestyle if you learned how to quickly prepare these meals and truly enjoyed them!

Some cookbooks overwhelm you with too many recipes! More recipes won't help you eat better, but learning the basics of putting a meal together when you're short on time will. You don't need 100 smoothie recipes. You just need a few good recipes and suggestions on how to switch things up.

Most cookbooks don't tell you how to combine recipes into a complete meal. To simplify meal planning, I give you suggestions for recipes to pair together for balanced and appetizing meals..

Many recipes, especially smoothies and juices, include more sugar than your body needs. If you tend to crash after meals or get hungry very quickly, it's probably because you eat too many carbs and not enough protein. All my recipes help balance blood sugar so you have a steady energy supply and fewer cravings.

After years of adjusting meals for my patients and scribbling recipes on scrap paper in my office, I finally have all my detox, delicious, and easy recipes in one book that you can enjoy as well.

Preparing the recipes will not take too much of your time. I'm passionate about food and cooking, and I won't sacrifice health or flavor. But as a mom, constantly juggling family, work, and fun, I can't spend hours in the kitchen. The recipes in the book are from my simple kitchen to yours. They help me put delicious meals on the table and I'm confident they will help you too.

Don't be scared if you see a recipe with more than 10 ingredients. I use several herbs and spices, and the variety helps your body detox and adds layers of flavor to your meals! These spices and herbs can be found in all grocery stores. They are worth the investment because you will use them often. I also usually include several vegetables in a meal to add more flavor, texture, nutrients, and color appeal.

All the recipes are free of gluten, dairy, soy, corn, peanuts, artificial ingredients, fried foods, and sugars (except for honey or 100% maple syrup occasionally). These foods tend to promote inflammation and food sensitivities, bog down detoxification, damage the gut, and hinder digestion. You might be able to tolerate some of them in small amounts, but you'll have to find that out for yourself. Try removing these foods for few weeks using *The Detox Way* recipes. Add them back later and monitor how you feel. You're not depriving yourself from anything! Think of what you will gain and how your body might feel when nourished with detox clean foods!

The Detox Way has a variety of recipes with different flavors from different cuisines. Variety keeps your meals interesting and helps you make this way of eating

a lifestyle. You don't have to drink juice cleanses or lemon water all day long. You don't have to eat salads all the time. And you don't need to buy expensive ingredients either.

Whenever possible, I included suggestions for substitutions. If you don't have an ingredient, don't like an ingredient (although I challenge you to keep an open mind), have allergies to an ingredient, or if another is in season, you can easily make simple and balanced swaps.

I sincerely hope you benefit from this book and savor scrumptious meals while you give your body the opportunity to feel energized, focused, and physically and mentally empowered. I would love to hear from you, so don't hesitate to connect through my website or social media.

Lots of Love,

Nour

Nour Zibdeh, MS RDN CLT
Functional Nutritionist and Dietitian
www.NourZibdeh.com

Learn

BALANCE YOUR MEALS

WHAT BALANCE MEANS AND WHY IT MATTERS

Many of us are looking for the next best thing to lose weight, feel great, and have more energy. Yet the answer is right here in front of us. Balance. Crafting meals with the right proportion of nutrients is the foundation of any eating plan, whether it's a gluten-free, dairy-free, digestive friendly, heart healthy, diabetes or anything else.

WHAT DOES BALANCE MEAN?

In my book, when I refer to balance, I mean balancing macronutrients through balancing food groups. You can balance your meals without tracking calories, points, or writing journals.

WHY BALANCE?

For a variety of reasons. First, let's go over what macronutrients are and what foods contain them.

Macronutrients are carbohydrates, fats, and proteins. These three are the only sources of energy (calories) to fuel our bodies. Micronutrients, on the other hand, are vitamin, minerals, anti-oxidants, and other co-factors that don't supply energy. They are critical for many functions and pathways, and necessary for building several different tissues.

Balancing macronutrients will impact your health on many different aspects. It will prevent crashes, increase fullness, reduce cravings, improve weight loss, and so forth. But we taste, touch, feel, and smell food, not amino acids, fatty acids, or disaccharides. So the conversation has to be about food.

But food can be complex. It's impossible to categorize each and every food under one specific macronutrient group. Some foods are easy. Olive oil for example is made of 100% fats. But things like fish, meats, beans, nuts, seeds, grains, yogurt, and cheese have a combination of macronutrients. They fit into several groups. How do you go about balancing your meals then?

I have been using a plate method for balancing meals and it has helped many of my patients improve their eating habits. This way of eating ensures:
  • Loading on vegetables, fiber, and antioxidants
  • Staying full for longer
  • Eating more food but fewer calories
  • Preventing cravings and blood sugar dips
  • Having constant supply of energy and

preventing crashes

Based on this approach, every meal needs to have four important parts:
- Vegetables: half of your plate
- Proteins: quarter of your plate
- Carbohydrates: quarter of your plate
- Fats: use as a condiment

The plate picture is a template of how each meal should look like. Many of us are visual learners, and not everyone wants to or has the time to measure every spoonful of food. Any time you sit down to eat, ask yourself, 'does my plate have vegetables? Do I have a balance of protein and carbohydrates? Did I add some fats in cooking or as a condiment?'

The balanced plate I use and recommend is different from USDA's 'My Plate'. If you look at any 'My Plate' graphics, you will see that fruits, grains, and dairy make up half of the plate. That is way too many carbohydrates in one meal! Note that yogurt and milk have natural sugars that will contribute to the total sugar load of your meal. According to MyPlate, starchy vegetables like potatoes, winter squashes, beets, and corn fall under the vegetable group. MyPlate also doesn't point to carbohydrate-heavy proteins like beans, peas, and

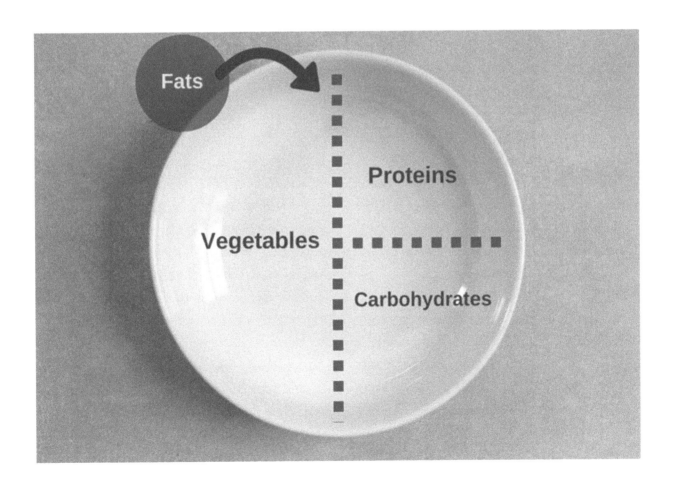

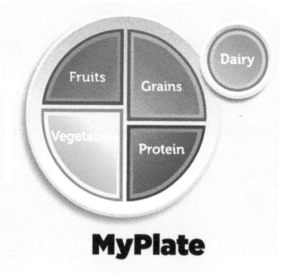

MyPlate

- Recommends fruits and grains in the SAME meal.
- Starchy vegetables, like potatoes, winter squashes, corn, and others are counted under vegetables.
- Starch-heavy proteins, like beans and lentils, are under protein and no emphasis on their carbohydrate content.
- Dairy is needed as part of a healthy meal.
- No mention of fats, sources, and amount to eat.

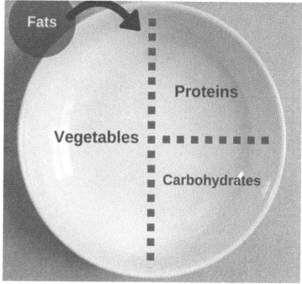

- Choose either fruit or grain.
- Starchy vegetables are counted under carbohydrates.
- Starch-heavy proteins usually count under carbohydrates. If they are the only source of protein, skip other carbohydrates.
- Dairy is not mandatory. Include if tolerated. Count cheese as protein and fat, milk or yogurt as protein and carbohydrates.
- Fats are included, with info on best sources and amount.

lentils. You can easily overeat carbohydrates if you follow MyPlate.

Another important difference between my balanced detox plate and USDA's MyPlate is the amount of vegetables. I recommend half the plate to be non-starchy vegetables alone, not a combination of fruits and vegetables. That will help keep the sugar and calorie content of meals lower.

Through helping my patients lose weight and balance sugar and energy levels, I noticed that a big percent ate too many carbohydrates, which can hinder weight loss efforts. They were under the impression that 'complex' carbohydrates or whole grains are good, so they didn't limit the amount they ate. They didn't know that in excess, even these carbohydrates create blood sugar problems.

Eating too many carbohydrates has its downside. When you eat a lot of carbohydrates and sugars, both processed and natural, the body will respond by releasing insulin. It's that hormone that signals your body to shuttle glucose into your cells. Frequent and high insulin release has been associated with damage to nerve cells (which has been linked to Alzheimer's disease), and faster aging. Too much insulin too frequently in the day will shut down fat tissue breakdown. This is because it signals the body that food is here and abundant. The body responds by locking the fat in our love handles and muffin tops because we can reserve the energy there for a rainier day.

The balanced detox plate I use focuses on non-starchy vegetables instead. Fruits, grains, dairy (if you choose to consume), beans, lentils, and non-starchy vegetables all fall in one quarter of your plate. You can't have all of them in one meal! Healthy proteins make up the remainder of the plate to ensure satiety. Fats are a condiment that adds flavor, improves satiety, and helps your body absorb certain vitamins and antioxidants. I discuss each category in more details next.

VEGETABLES

If you don't like vegetables, it's probably because you've never had them prepared in a good way. If you didn't eat too many vegetables growing up, it can be a new learning experience. Keep an open mind and have fun experimenting.

Non-starchy vegetables need to make up half of each meal. Non-starchy vegetables include produce like broccoli, cauliflower, green beans, mushrooms, tomatoes, spinach, kale, and many more. They are packed with water and fiber that will keep you feeling full for longer. A cup of non-starchy vegetables contributes very little calories compared to a cup of fruit, beans, chicken, rice, or nuts. That means you can feed your body a generous amount of vegetables, eat more volume and feel full without worrying about eating too many calories.

These vegetables are the foundation of an anti-inflammatory way of eating. They supply the body with vitamins, minerals, polyphenols, antioxidants, and co-factors that reduce inflammation and support detoxification.

We have to get vitamins from food because our bodies cannot make them internally. There are two types of vitamins, water-soluble and fat-soluble. Water-soluble vitamins are B vitamins and vitamin C. They cannot be stored in the body in large quantities, so it's important that we eat foods rich in these vitamins every single day. A cup of bell peppers, broccoli, or Brussels sprouts has more vitamin C than a cup of strawberries or oranges! Folate, one of the B vitamins, is found in spinach, parsley, broccoli, mustard greens, asparagus, and lettuce. Vitamin B_6 is found in bell peppers, turnip greens, and spinach. Vitamin B_2 is found in spinach, beet greens, mushrooms, and asparagus.

These vitamins orchestrate hundreds of roles and pathways in your body. They are needed to extract energy from food, reproduce healthy DNA to repair damaged tissue, heal skin wounds, produce healthy intestinal cell lining, boost your immune system, promote phase 1 in liver detoxification, and so much more. If you feel tired, have digestive complains, or get sick too often, chances are you're running low on

some vitamins stores.

But vitamins aren't the only good things about vegetables. Vegetables are abundant in very crucial compounds called phytonutrients, which are a category of antioxidants. Different phytonutrients give vegetables their unique colors. If you've heard that you need to eat a rainbow of vegetables, it's because these colors correlate to different antioxidants. In a simplistic manner, these different color-based antioxidants correlate to different health benefits:

- White: immune support
- Yellow: beauty, skin elasticity, detoxification
- Green: detoxification and liver

support
- Red: heart and prostate health
- Purple: longevity, anti-aging, cancer prevention
- Orange: cancer prevention

Plus, a beautiful colorful plate is always more appealing. We do eat with our eyes first!

Vegetables supply your body with antioxidants and polyphenols. Antioxidants neutralize free radicals and other harmful species that develop as your body metabolizes nutrients, extracts energy, detoxes chemicals, and so forth. They prevent inflammation and damage to arteries, tissues, and cell membranes. Since these pathways are running 24 hours a day, it's not enough to eat vegetables at dinnertime only.

Both raw and cooked vegetables have health benefits and I suggest a mix of the two. Raw vegetables have a high water and fiber content. They are more filling and hydrating. They help improve bowel movements. People often enjoy the texture, crunch and cooling effect of raw vegetables.

When vegetables are cooked, their cell walls get broken down. They become easier to digest and the nutrients can be extracted and absorbed more efficiently. This is helpful for people with digestive or absorption issues like inflammatory bowel disease (IBD), irritable bowel syndrome, or leaky gut.

Raw vegetables retain antioxidants and protective compounds content. Cooking destroys vitamin C and increases the rate of its oxidation (reaction with oxygen). Cooking broccoli reduces the level of compounds that fights pre-cancerous cells as well as the bacteria *Helicobacter pylori* (H pylori), which causes ulcers and increases the risk of stomach cancer. Raw carrots have more polyphenols (antioxidants)

than cooked carrots. And several studies show that the content of antioxidants and health-promoting compounds in broccoli and red cabbage is reduced with cooking.

However, cooking activates different nutrients in vegetables. For example, cooked tomatoes have 35% more lycopene compared to raw tomatoes[1], and carrots blanched for a short period of time have more beta-carotene (vitamin A precursor) than raw carrots[2].

The cooking method and time impact nutrient retention of vegetables. Some studies find steaming to be best, others recommend sautéing without too much water, and some even report more nutrient retention with microwaving. Boiling causes a lot of nutrients, such as vitamin C and chlorophyll to be lost in the water. You lose amazing antioxidants when you discard the green water you boiled broccoli in!

In general, my preferred methods are steaming and quick sautéing. Don't overcook your vegetables when you steam or saute them. Cook them long enough so they soften but short enough so they stay crunchy, usually less than 10 minutes. And always use as little water as possible, unless you plan to use this water and make a stew.

As you can see, there's no one way to eating your vegetables. Some nutrients are activated while others are destroyed with cooking. Since the best vegetable for you is the vegetable you actually eat, choose the cooking method that is most appealing to you and that will encourage you to eat more vegetables!

In the cheat sheets section, I give you a list of non-starchy vegetables grouped by their color.

PROTEIN

Protein has so many health benefits. I typically recommend more protein than government guidelines as long as they come from clean sources. If you have kidney disease, liver disease, or gout, you need different and individualized protein recommendations, and the discussion here does not apply to you.

First, let's talk about what the guidelines say. The Institute of Medicine (IOM) set the Recommended Daily Allowance (RDA) for protein at 0.8 gram of protein per kilogram of body weight. That is 0.36 grams of protein per pound of body weight. Based on this calculation, if you weigh 140 pounds, you would need to eat 50 grams of protein each day.

However, this recommendation by the IOM is the minimum amount needed to prevent protein deficiency, not promote optimal health. My experience working with clients and patients over the years confirms that more protein is needed. The RDA amount is not enough if you want to lose weight, build muscle, or heal and repair tissue. I generally recommend 1.5 grams of protein per kilogram of body weight, which is about 0.68 grams of protein per pound of body weight. If you weigh 140 pounds, I recommend 95 grams of protein a day. That's almost double the RDA amount.

Is that too much protein? As long as you don't have kidney or liver disease, or any other condition that requires that you limit protein, and you stick to the general guidelines I'm about to share with you, eating slightly more protein than the RDA amount does not pose a health risk. Keep in mind that there's an upper limit, which is 2 grams of protein per kilogram of body weight or 0.9 grams of protein per pound of body weight. For example, if you weigh 140 pounds, don't eat more than 130 grams proteins a day.

General guidelines for increasing the protein in your diet:
- Eat slightly less carbohydrates so you don't overeat calories
- Vary your protein sources to include both animal and plant sources
- Choose lean animal proteins more often, like fish, shellfish, chicken, and turkey
- You can eat red meats 2–3 times a week, but when you do, choose lean cuts and grass-fed options. Always pair meats with vegetables
- Drink plenty of water

Protein from food supplies the body with 20 different amino acids, the building blocks of almost everything in your body. Your muscles, bones, glands, cells membranes, skin, hair, nails, eyes, vital organs, digestive system, immune cells, hormones, enzymes, and neurotransmitters are made of amino acids. We need to eat protein daily because our bodies can't easily store and access them.

Amino acids are grouped based on whether they can be made in our bodies or not. Nine of the 20 amino acids are 'essential.' They have to be obtained from food because the body can't make them by itself. The remaining 11 amino acids are 'non-essential' and the body can create them from other amino acids. However, in times of stress, illness, or scarcity, some 'non-essential' amino acids become 'conditionally essential' because their building blocks aren't available. In that case, these must be obtained from food as well. This distinction will be important when we talk about animal vs. plant proteins later.

Protein is crucial for building new muscles and preserving those you already have. We all start to lose muscle mass starting at the age of 30. A diet that provides an optimal amount of protein—along with resistance training—will help prevent muscle losses. Strong muscles improve your balance and stability, reduce the likelihood of falling, and improve your ability to recover if you fall. Strong muscles help strengthen your bones and reduce the risk of fractures.

Studies show that high protein diets protect from muscle loss in the elderly, prevent hip fractures, and promote wound healing.

Protein can also help you lose weight. Studies show that people are more satisfied when they eat high protein meals compared to when they eat meals high in carbohydrates. Fats tend to make you less satiated than protein but more than carbohydrates. To put it into perspective, 150 calories from protein (ex. 3–4 ounces of grilled chicken) are going to satisfy you more and keep you full longer than 150 calories from carbohydrates (ex. ⅔ cup rice). When people eat a good amount of protein at a meal, they tend to eat less at that meal and at subsequent meals.

Another way protein can help you lose weight is through dietary thermogenesis, also called the thermic effect of food. This is the amount of energy the body will spend in order to digest and absorb food. While it varies between one person and another, the thermic effect of protein is about 20–35% of the calories you eat, while the thermic effect of fats and carbohydrates is about 5–10%. To put it into perspective, if you eat 200 calories of protein, your body will burn 40–70 calories just to process it. If you eat 200 calories of fat or carbohydrates, you will only burn 10–20 calories to process them.

Most people who want to lose weight start with significant calorie restriction.

Because your internal organs still need energy to function, your body will use any amino acids in your diet for energy, instead of allowing them to build enzymes, hormones, and other critical roles. To compensate, your muscles get broken down to provide amino acids. With prolonged low calorie intake without optimal protein, you will lose muscle mass as you lose weight. Several studies confirm that and find that high protein diets, along with resistance training, with modest (not extreme) calorie reduction help protect muscle losses.

What adds insult to injury is that most people regain the weight they lost, especially if it was quick weight loss or not a lifestyle change. When they regain the weight, it's not muscle weight. It's more weight in their fat tissue—love handles, around the belly, thighs, etc.! Few years of yo-yo dieting and weight loss and weight gain cycles will make you lose muscle mass and gain fat tissue. And we know muscles burn more calories. If you compare two women with same age, height, and weight, the woman who had several weight loss and regain cycles will burn fewer calories than the woman who had never even tried to lose weight. This can be discouraging, but the lesson learned is that protecting your muscle mass through optimal protein intake and resistance training is very important.

Another benefit of protein is that it helps manage blood sugar. Protein (in addition to fats and fiber) slows down the rate at which your body absorbs glucose. When you eat a carbohydrate-rich meal without protein (or fat), your blood sugar will spike within 30 minutes. This will happen even if the carbohydrate is healthy like a piece of fruit. Your pancreas will respond by pushing a lot of insulin into the blood stream to make the glucose go inside the cells and bring your blood sugar back to normal. Too much insulin will not help you lose weight because it will prevent fat tissue from being used up for energy. Instead, it will make you store more fat. I will talk more about insulin in the carbohydrate section.

Protein comes from animal and plant foods. Animal proteins are considered complete because they contain all 20 essential amino acids. Plant proteins, such as beans, grains, nuts, seeds, and some vegetables, lack one or more of the essential amino acids. If you've heard that you need to combine two plant proteins at the same meal, it's to compensate for the lack of any essential amino acids and make a complete protein meal. But you don't need to pair plant proteins at the *same* meal. As long as your body has all essential amino acids *within the whole day*, you should be good.

I have been studying nutrition for over 10 years and practicing for 8 years. I started out against animal proteins. However, my years of experience working with people with different health issues and concerns taught me that incorporating high quality clean animal proteins is more advantageous than completely eliminating them. A medium amount of animal protein goes a long way to provide you with the essential nutrients like vitamin B_{12}, zinc, iron, vitamin D, and amino acids.

Animal proteins don't have sugars or starches so they boost the protein content of your meal without adding carbohydrates. This is helpful for people with diabetes, pre-diabetes, polycystic ovarian syndrome, or anyone who needs to be strict about managing their blood sugar. People with digestive complaints like irritable bowel syndrome or auto-immune conditions like Hashimoto's or Crohn's disease typically tolerate chicken, fish, eggs, and meat more than plant-based proteins like beans, grains, nuts or seeds.

The *Healthy Proteins* in the cheat sheets section shows the different types of animal and plant-based proteins. I usually recommend about 18–28 grams of protein at meals and 7–15 grams of protein at snacks.

The quality of your animal proteins depends on how they were grown. Pasture chicken and eggs, where chickens roam and eat their natural diet, are superior to conventionally grown chicken crammed into tight pens, fed synthetic grains, and treated excessively with antibiotics. Beef from grass-fed beef cows has a healthy fatty acid profile compared to cows conventionally raised and fed wheat, soy, and corn grains to get fattened or marbled. Wild-caught fish is preferred over farm-raised fish.

I am aware of the terrible ways conventional animals are raised to generate more profit for large corporations. I do not support animal cruelty and we have to demand humanely raised animals. We have to make an effort to find and support farmers that do. Start at your grocery store, health food store, or butcher shops. Ask them where the meat came from and how it was raised. You can join a local co-op or buy directly from farms. Check Local harvest (www.localharvest.com) to find farmers and sustainable options near you. There are also several options for shopping online.

Eggs are an excellent convenient and inexpensive source of complete protein. Several studies showed that eating up to 3 eggs a day for 6 weeks didn't raise cholesterol in both healthy individuals and in people with high cholesterol[3,4,5]. Egg yolks are an excellent source of choline, a nutrient classified like a vitamin. It's necessary for the communication between nerve cells, the structure and health of cell membranes, and the metabolism of fats in the liver. In fact, choline deficiency can cause chronic liver damage.

You can enjoy eggs in many different ways. The easiest and fastest way is to hard-boil a batch for the whole week on the weekend. They would last peeled in your fridge for 3–5 days. You can add them to salads or combine them with roasted vegetables

for a quick weekday lunch. They're also an excellent snack. Frittata is another favorite because you can make it on Sunday morning and have it for breakfast or lunch the following day or two. There's a frittata recipe in the breakfast section of this book.

There are several ways to prepare fish, poultry, and red meats. Moist and indirect cooking at low temperatures like simmering, sautéing, poaching, braising, slow cooking, baking with some liquid, and stewing are my preferred methods.

Dry and direct cooking at high

temperatures, like grilling and broiling, can lead to formation of heterocyclic amines (HCAs) and polycyclic aromatic hydrocarbons (PAHs) that damage DNA and increase cancer risks. The longer the meat is cooked, the more HCAs and PAHs that develop. They will develop whether you cook on a grill in open flames or direct heat like a stovetop grill pan or electric grill.

Another troubling compound is advanced glycation products (AGEs) that contribute to inflammation and chronic conditions. They develop when proteins and sugars in food react together at high temperatures. They also develop in commercially roasted nuts and conventional refined oils.

There are ways to reduce the concentrations of HCAs, PAHs, and AGEs in your diet so you can enjoy and benefit from animal proteins. First, meats should only make up a quarter of your plate. Non-starchy vegetables, which clean out toxins and fight free radicals, should make up the majority of your meal. In my book, all my recipes are made with lots of vegetables or I give you suggestions for vegetable recipes to pair with protein recipes.

Instead of grilling, try braising, boiling, steaming and other liquid-based cooking methods that produce less HCAs, PAHs, and AGEs more often. If you grill, don't overcook the meat, don't let it char, and don't eat charred parts. When you bake or roast, add some water to the pan and roast at the lowest temperature possible. Marinate meats in some acid like lemon or vinegar to reduce AGEs formation. Avoid deep-frying altogether.

Keep in mind that processed foods have even more HCAs, PAHs, and AGEs than cooked meats. That's because they are processed at high temperatures. Removing those and eating fresh will help you reduce the overall amount of damaging and inflammatory compounds in your diet.

Let's move to plant proteins. Beans, lentils, and peas are the best plant protein sources. Grains like quinoa, steel-cut oats, and buckwheat, have more protein than wheat, rice, and corn. When you use beans or grains in a meal, count them as a carbohydrate, not protein. If you're having a vegetarian meal and counting bean as your protein, be careful not to add more carbohydrates like rice, bread, fruit, or potatoes. Carbohydrates will easily add up and make an unbalanced meal.

Beans and lentils add healthy fiber to the diet. While this is usually a good thing, people with digestive discomforts like irritable bowel syndrome (IBS), inflammatory bowel disease (IBD), or anyone complaining of gas, bloating, constipation, diarrhea, or cramps have trouble digesting beans. And I see more and more patients with these complaints every day. Government and media advice us to eat a lot of beans, and some people take that to heart and force beans down even though their bodies are clearly not tolerating them.

Compounds in beans and grains called lectins are the reason why these foods are problematic. They are naturally hard to digest, especially for people with any gut inflammation. In the gut, bacteria ferment lectins, producing gases that cause bloating, pain, gas, diarrhea, and/or constipation. For some people, exposure to lectins promotes the growth of unfavorable bacteria and leads to gut dysbiosis, a term that means you have an imbalance between healthy and unhealthy bacteria.

Lectins can irritate the lining of the intestines, contributing to leaky gut or as known medically intestinal permeability. This means the barrier between the content of your gut and the rest of your body is damaged. Microbes and their toxins, undigested food particles, and any chemicals in your food that were kept outside are able to enter your body and create havoc. The immune system gets activated and may result in food sensitivities. The symptoms can be digestive trouble or non-digestion related like headache, fatigue, brain fog, muscle pain, or others. Sometimes, leaky gut triggers auto-immune conditions like Crohn's or Hashimoto's.

Lectins, phytates, and other fibers in beans prevent the release of nutrients. This makes it difficult for your intestinal cells obtain any vitamins, minerals, and antioxidants. Despite being an excellent source of folate, for example, it's not easy to tell how much is actually absorbed.

Gut healing and digestive protocols are not the purpose of this book. If you can't tolerate beans and grains, or if you have a digestive or autoimmune condition, you need a customized meal plan. Visit my website at www.nourzibdeh.com/healthygut and www.nourzibdeh.com/autoimmune for information specific to these conditions.

To make nutrients more available and improve your ability to digest beans, soak them in water for 8 hours or overnight. Discard the soaking water before cooking. In the basic recipes section, I include two recipes for cooking beans. Beans from scratch are better than canned because most cans contain toxic BPA, unless they specify BPA-free. Canned beans are more expensive and have more salt and preservatives. Cook them in large batches and freeze the extra in glass jars for later. Lentils cook so fast and don't need to be soaked overnight.

If you can tolerate beans, pair them with chicken fajita, grilled chicken, baked fish, and salads. They can be a snack on their own too. A half-cup of chickpeas with freshly squeezed lemon juice, cumin, and salt will give you about 8 grams of protein and 20 grams carbohydrates (just the right amount for a snack). Peas are great in soups, stews, stir-fries, and egg frittata. I usually have a bag in the freezer that I add to leftover chicken and vegetables for a quick easy dinner.

Soy is another plant protein source, but I recommend avoiding it. More than 90% of the soy produced in the US is genetically modified. The crops are sprayed with the herbicide Roundup, which has detrimental effects on human health. Soybeans contain compounds called isoflavones that resemble the shape of estrogen (one of the female sex hormone) and disrupt hormone balance. Isoflavones attach to estrogen receptors in the body, blocking the real hormone from working. Sometimes, they unfavorably increase the activity of estrogen and its receptors. Some studies show that isoflavones can stimulate the growth of cancerous cells in the breast.

The majority of soy in Western diets is in the form of isolated soy protein in protein bars, veggie patties, soymilk, and other products that people mistakenly consider healthy. Isolated soy protein is made from soybean meal, which is what remains of the beans after the oil has been extracted. The soybean meal is either used to feed conventionally grown livestock or further processed to make isolated soy protein powder. It's a cheap protein filler in our food system.

Asian cultures have a lower rate of cancer than Western countries. Some contribute this benefit to soy isoflavones, claiming that soy is healthy. However, these cultures eat whole and fermented soy like soy sauce, tempeh, and miso, which might be beneficial in small amounts. They don't eat processed isolated soy meal and soy powder! None of the recipes in The Detox Way use any soy products.

Nuts and seeds are a decent source of protein. Almonds, pumpkin seeds, and hemp seeds contain the highest amount of protein per weight. The reason I say 'decent' and not 'high' source is because you need to eat a lot to get 18 grams of protein, the minimum amount I recommend for meals. That means your meals will be very calorie-dense. To get 15 grams of protein, you would need to eat 60 almonds, which also contain whopping 400 calories. Overeating nuts is one the most common reasons people who start eating healthy gain weight! Large amounts of nuts and seeds can also cause gas, bloating, or stomach or intestinal cramps. When planning meals, consider them as a healthy fat option and enjoy them with other protein sources. As a snack, measure how much you eat and stick to two tablespoons of nuts.

CARBOHYDRATES

We have already brought up carbohydrates in the proteins section and we will continue to build on that here.

If you do a quick online search, you'll find recommendations that range from banning carbohydrates completely to others that recommend the majority of your meals to come from carbohydrates. It's confusing and frustrating.

My experience over the years taught me that different people need different amounts and types of carbohydrates. Even the same person may need different amounts at different times of their lives.

I generally recommend a low to moderate amount of healthy carbohydrates. Very low or no carbohydrate diets stress your thyroid and adrenal glands. Long-term restriction can eventually trigger chronic adrenal fatigue and thyroid problems like hypothyroidism, which will lower your metabolism and how much energy you burn. Carbohydrates have a calming effect because they induce the secretion of serotonin, one of the neurotransmitters that make you feel good. When you completely eliminate carbohydrates, you might notice yourself becoming more anxious and irritable, and might end up with even more cravings and emotional eating. People who go on very low carbohydrates diet report reduced energy and not being able to keep up with exercise.

That doesn't mean I never use very low carbohydrates approach. Eliminating carbohydrates for a short period of time can help boost weight loss. I don't typically start with very low carbohydrates diets because there won't be room to go lower if needed. But if you've reached a plateau, reducing carbohydrates even further for a short period of time can help you get unstuck. I've recommended to some patients in the past to remove carbohydrates from breakfast or dinner so they trigger their bodies to burn fat tissue. It's often very individual.

Additionally, if I suspect candida (yeast) overgrowth, dysbiosis, or small intestinal bacterial overgrowth (SIBO), I may remove carbohydrates completely. These conditions cause digestive discomforts, and if you suspect you have one of them, visit my website at http://www.nourzibdeh. com/healthygut/ for an individualized approach.

As a starting point, I typically recommend that 40% of calories come from carbohydrates to keep meals balanced. To translate that to food, that is about 2 carbohydrate options at meals and 1 carbohydrate option at snacks. If you're a very active person, you can probably fit more in your meals and snacks. The Healthy Carbohydrates cheat sheet shows you healthy carbohydrate options and portions.

Visually, you can use my balanced plate method and limit your carbohydrates to a quarter of your plate. This is easy if your meal consists of three different items like chicken, broccoli, and potato. If you make soup, casserole, or stew, make sure that carbohydrate foods do not make up the majority of the meal or ingredients. You're eating too much carbohydrate if your casserole is mostly potatoes, peas, and corn. All the meals in this book are balanced to have about 40% of carbohydrates.

Any time you eat a carbohydrate food, your body releases insulin from your pancreas to transport the glucose you just absorbed inside your cells. Every carbohydrate food, including fruit, complex carbohydrates, beans, whole grains, brown rice, etc. will

eventually be digested and broken down to glucose. It's not just from sweets and sugars!

If there's too much glucose in the blood, the pancreas will react by overproducing insulin. Too much insulin will drop your blood sugar level too quickly, and you might feel like you've crashed. I'm sure you've experienced that after eating a large piece of dessert.

If you continue to eat excessive amounts of carbohydrates, the pancreas will continue to overproduce insulin. At some point, the cells in your body become insensitive to insulin, meaning that they can't see it. So your pancreas has to secrete even more insulin to drop your blood sugar level to normal. This is known as insulin sensitivity, which is the first step towards developing diabetes.

Insulin is a hormone that communicates messages to the rest of your body. When there's insulin in your blood all the time, it's communicating to your fat tissue that food and energy are present, and there's no need to break down fat tissue to extract energy. In fact, insulin promotes further fat storage.

This is one of the reasons I don't support constant snacking or grazing. When you eat too often during the day, your body is constantly sensing insulin. I typically recommend three good meals and one or potentially two snacks a day that are at least

3–4 hours apart. I also recommend at least 10 hours before your last meal or snack for the day and next-day's breakfast. That will allow your body a break from insulin.

Choosing your carbohydrates wisely will prevent a quick spike in blood sugar. Carbohydrates with high fiber and protein content like quinoa or beans are best. Pairing carbohydrates with protein or fat foods will slow down how fast you absorb glucose. That's why my balanced plate method includes an equal amount of protein and carbohydrates. The Healthy Snack Builder cheat sheet follows the same principle as I show you what to pair with fruit to make a balanced snack.

We can all agree that processed carbohydrates, like pastries, muffins, cookies, crackers, sweets, and sugars are not the wisest options. I also add breads, pastas, wraps, breakfast cereals, and rice—even whole grain—to the list of carbs to avoid. They are highly processed, contain little nutrition, and will eventually be broken down to glucose. In fact, a slice of bread contains the same amount of sugar as two tablespoons of sugar. Commercial breads typically contain undesirable ingredients like brominated vegetable oil (disrupts thyroid function), soybean oil (genetically modified), partially hydrogenated vegetable oils (trans fats), fully hydrogenated vegetable oils (man-made saturated fats), dough conditions, preservatives, sugars, and others.

If you can tolerate bread and gluten, consider it an occasional treat, not a staple. Only eat fresh delicious bread that's worth every bite! Consider sourdough bread since it's fermented or sprouted breads because they contain more nutrients and are easier to digest. If you can't tolerate gluten and eat gluten-free varieties, remember that gluten-free breads are still processed and should be enjoyed occasionally.

In the cheat sheet section, I give you a list of healthy carbohydrates with serving sizes. Healthy carbohydrates are those packed with vitamins and minerals and contain fiber and/or protein to help balance blood sugar. These are starchy vegetables like winter squashes, beets, and sweet potatoes,

legumes like beans and lentils, and whole grains like steel-cut or rolled oats, quinoa, and buckwheat, and fruit with low glycemic index. These carbohydrates prevent sugar crashes, provide you with a steady source of energy, and prevent chronic diseases diabetes, heart disease, and cancers.

In the cheat sheet, I divide fruits into two groups; high and low glycemic index. High glycemic index foods raise blood sugar quickly, while low glycemic index foods are desirable because they raise blood sugar slowly. Choose fruits from the low glycemic index list more often. Keep in mind that pairing fruit with fats and proteins like nuts will reduce the glycemic load of the meal, which is more meaningful than looking at fruit alone.

This book contains several recipes with healthy carbohydrates. Sweet potato is an easy and delicious side in many of the dishes. Quinoa mixed with vegetables and some shrimp or scrambled eggs (just like fried rice) is a great quick lunch. Buckwheat groats, or kasha, can replace rice for more protein and nutrients. Fresh beets or fruit in a salad add some sweetness and boost antioxidants. Different kinds of beans can be used in salads, snacks, or main dishes. You won't sacrifice flavor when you eliminate processed carbohydrates!

Corn is one of those controversial foods that I would like to address. Most of the corn in our diet, about 90%, is genetically modified and contains BT toxin. BT stands for Bacillus thuringiensis, a bacterium that naturally produces toxin-releasing proteins that kill pests and insects. When an insect eats GMO corn, the toxin paralyzes its digestive tract and creates pores in its gut lining, leading to its death.

While GMO-corn manufacturers claim that it's safe for human consumption, I lean towards being more cautious. The toxin can have a similar effect on the human gut, causing holes or punctures and leading to leaky gut, inflammation, food sensitivities, and autoimmune conditions. A study in Canada showed that the BT toxin has been detected in the blood of pregnant women and their fetuses.[4] Another study found that the BT toxin triggered hematotoxicity (destruction in red blood cells) in mice and concluded that its effect on humans is still unknown.[6,7]

For these reasons, I recommend limiting the amount of corn you eat. The majority of corn in our diet is in the form of corn syrup, high fructose corn syrup (HFCS), and other compounds derived from corn like citric acid, dextrose, artificial sweeteners, and more. Eliminating those would be the first step.

If you have digestive problems, stay away from corn. If you don't have digestive issues and would like to eat corn, stick to organic varieties because they are not genetically modified (although no guarantees can be made about GMO seeds flying from one field to another). If you like popcorn or corn chips, let them be occasional treats and not daily snacks. Enjoy corn on the cob in the summer when it's in season, but pass on canned and frozen corn that aren't as delicious. The nutrient content in corn is less impressive than fruit or starchy vegetables like sweet potatoes or winter squashes. Because I eliminate corn on the full medical detox program I use with my patients, I decided to not use corn in any of the recipes.

FATS

Eating fat will not make you fat. Good fats are good for you and bad fats are bad for you. You just need to know which ones are which. In the cheat sheet section, you have two resources for fats, *Healthy Fats List and Best Oils for Cooking and Salads.*

There are two types of fats to strictly avoid, trans fats and processed vegetable oils.

Trans-fats are created when vegetables oils are hydrogenated, the process in which hydrogen atoms are added to liquid oils to make them solid. Trans fats in our diet come from using products like shortening or margarine or eating commercial products that are made with them.

Shortening gained popularity from food companies because it improved their profit margins. It's inexpensive because it came from government-subsidized surpluses of soy, corn, and cottonseed oils. When used in muffins, biscuits, cookies and other baked goods, it enhances flavor, moisture, and richness, so consumers enjoy and buy more of these products. Shortening doesn't need refrigeration and increases the shelf life of processed foods.

But what improves companies' bottom lines usually doesn't improve health or our waistlines. Trans fats increase of getting and dying from coronary heart disease.[8] They trigger the body to store fat around the belly and promote inflammation, the leading cause of diabetes, heart disease, arthritis, cancers, and other chronic inflammatory conditions. It's recommended to consume zero trans fats.

It's not enough to remove shortening or margarine from your kitchen. Despite the push against trans fats, they are still in the food system. To eliminate them completely, you need to become a food label detective. By law, if a serving contains less than 0.5 grams of trans fats, a manufacturer can list '0 trans-fat' in the Nutrition Facts Panel and plaster that all over the package. Some manufacturers reduce serving sizes to make the cut. But these serving sizes are often much smaller than the portion that someone might typically eat.

That's why you can't just count on what the label or health claims tell you. You must flip the package and look at the ingredients list. If you see 'partially hydrogenated' oil, put it back on the shelf. It's trans fats.

If you ever wondered what 'fully hydrogenated fats' are, they are manufactured to look like saturated fats. While still processed, they are not as bad as trans fats.

On a side note, dairy and meats from ruminant animals like cattle, sheep, and goat contain naturally occurring trans fats. Studies show that these natural trans fats are not associated with any increased risk of coronary heart disease. In fact, ruminant trans fats reduced the risk of type 2 diabetes.[6]

The second fats to avoid are vegetable oils like corn, soybean, and cottonseed oils. Because their seeds are hard, they have to be subjected to high temperatures, harsh chemicals, and solvents for their oils to be extracted. They are transferred in hot trucks and stored in plastic containers in hot warehouses. In the kitchen, they are used for high temperature cooking like frying. Exposure to heat and chemicals causes these oils to disintegrate before they even reach your body.

Vegetable oils are not healthy because they are concentrated in omega-6 fatty acids. They are not stable in heat because their chemical composition makes them susceptible to forming dangerous free radicals.

Omega-6 fatty acids are polyunsaturated fatty acids. There's so much confusion and misinformation about these oils, and I'm going to do my best to explain without going into too much detail. A specific omega-6 fatty acid, linoleic acid, is essential to the body and must obtained from the diet. It is converted to gamma-linolenic acid (GLA), which is another omega-6 needed to for skin and hair growth, bone heath, metabolism, and healthy reproductive system.

But some omega-6 fatty acids promote inflammation when they are converted to inflammatory compounds. Problems happen when there's too much omega-6 fatty acids and not enough omega-3 fatty acids, the other type of polyunsaturated fats that are anti-inflammatory.

A healthy omega-6 to omega-3 ratio in your diet and in your body is 4:1. When you consume foods high in omega-6 fatty acids, the ratio will go up, and that means inflammation. It's estimated that the average American diet has a high ratio between 7:1 and 13:1. I've tested many of my patients and have seen numbers that high.

Foods that contribute the most omega-6 fatty acids in our diet are vegetable oils like corn, soybean, and cottonseed oils and products made with them. Go around your kitchen and read ingredients lists. I challenge you that you have many products that contain these oils. Check commercial salad dressings, crackers, cookies, energy bars, potato chips, tortilla chips, frozen meals, and even some of your supplements.

Oils like sunflower, safflower, grapeseed, sesame, and walnuts oils also contain omega-6 fatty acids and will contribute to inflammation in excess. If you need to use those occasionally, choose products that are cold-pressed, meaning they were manufactured with low-temperatures and no chemicals. Buy them in a small amount in a dark glass bottle and finish them quickly. I don't have them in my kitchen and use olive and avocado oils instead.

The next type of fat I want to talk about is saturated fats. We have been told for 50 years that they are bad for our health and to avoid them to prevent heart disease. However, we have to question this presumed fact in light of emerging research.

Several studies found no association between saturated fats and the risk of coronary heart disease, cardiovascular disease, stroke, mortality, ischemic stroke, or type 2 diabetes.[8,9] A report by the World Health Organization concluded that the intake of saturated fats was not significantly associated with increased risk of dying from coronary heart disease or increased coronary heart disease events like heart attacks.[10]

It may even turn out that your cholesterol level has nothing to do with heart disease. A study found that half the people hospitalized for heart attacks had cholesterol and LDL (bad cholesterol) levels in the healthy ranges.[11] While the authors conclude that healthy ranges need to be lowered further, some argue that maybe cholesterol and LDL, the way they are traditionally measured, have noting to do with your risk of getting a heart attack.

Because of emerging research like these, I don't believe you need to cut all sources of saturated fats like red meat, butter, or coconut from your diet to improve your health. In fact, they are better for you than Franken foods made with synthetic and inflammatory ingredients.

At the same time, saturated fats aren't my first and daily choice and I don't recommend you include them liberally in your diet just yet. We don't know the whole story about saturated fats and the evidence to support the health benefits of monounsaturated fats, like olive and avocado, is stronger and clearer.

When authorities warn against red meat due to saturated fat content, there's often no distinction between grass-fed and conventionally grown grain-fed animals. Diets based on meats from grass-fed animals contain more conjugated linoleic acid (CLA), omega-3 fatty acids, vitamin A, vitamin E, and the antioxidants glutathione and superoxide dismutase compared to diets based on meats from grain-fed animals.[12] Dairy from grass-fed cows contains 500% more CLA than dairy from grain-fed cows.[13] Conjugated linoleic acid has health benefits such as reducing body fat and improving immune function, and it may even help reduce tumors.[14]

Coconut oil is a saturated fat and another controversial topic too. It is antimicrobial and helps fight viruses, fungi, and parasites. The majority of the saturated fatty acids in coconut oil, about 60%, are medium chain fatty acids, known as MCTs. They are absorbed directly from the gut and transported to the liver where they get utilized quickly for energy. Medium chain fatty acids are promoted for weight loss because they improve satiety, raise metabolic rate, and are less likely to be stored in fat tissue.

You might have heard of MCT oil supplements, so I want to briefly clarify any confusion between MCT oil and coconut oil. Coconut oil contains other types of saturated fats, whereas MCT oil supplements only contain MCTs. Concentrated MCT oil products are more potent for fat burning and improved satiety, coconut oil is a wholefood products that is also antimicrobial. If you're going to try a MCT oil supplement, look for a reputable supplier. You can contact us through the website for help.

As you can see, it's possible to enjoy good quality saturated fats a few times a week and reap some health benefits. Buy grass-fed animal products. I know they're more expensive but they are absolutely worth it.

Make sure the coconut oil you buy is cold-pressed. Just like any other type of fat, watch how much you eat! If you choose to experiment with coconut or MCT oil for weight loss, remove other sources of calories in your diet like unhealthy fats or sugars.

Next, I'm going to jump to omega-3 fatty acids. Found in fatty fish and some seeds like flaxseeds, they are anti-inflammatory and beneficial. Studies showed that they help lower triglycerides levels, reduce joint pain, and improve cognition, neurologic function, mood, and diabetes.

There are three omega-3 fatty acids: alpha-linolenic acid (ALA), which is plant-based, and Eicosapentaenoic acid (EPA) and Docosahexaenoic acid (DHA), which are marine-based. Flaxseeds are a good source of ALA, but they alone aren't enough. That's because EPA and DHA are the potent omega-3 fatty acids, and your body needs to convert ALA to EPA and DHA to reap any health benefits. But only 4–6% of ALA is converted to EPA and DHA, and this is further reduced if the diet is high on omega-6 fatty acids.

That's why incorporating fatty fish in your meal planning is important. For people who are generally healthy, two 4-ounce servings a week will provide enough EPA and DHA. Choose from herring, tuna, trout, salmon, mackerel (not king mackerel), anchovies, and sardines. The last two are great because they're small in size and contain very little mercury compared to larger fish.

If you have high triglycerides or an inflammatory condition, you may need extra omega-3's in the form of supplements. This is best discussed with a health professional. You can also contact us for help.

Finally, the last fat in this discussion is monounsaturated fats found in olives, olive oil, avocado, avocado oil, macadamia nuts, hazelnuts, and almonds. Research agrees that these oils have the most health benefits and pose no risk to our health. I count on them for the majority of meals and snacks.

Cooking with olive oil at low to medium temperatures without letting it smoke will not make it toxic. It will just be less nutritious. That's because heat reduces its polyphenols (antioxidants) content. To benefit more, drizzle olive oil over vegetables after they are finished roasting or steaming.

When buying olive oil, always choose

extra-virgin and cold-pressed products. 'Extra virgin' means it's extracted from the first press of olives and contains the most antioxidants. Cold-pressed means the oil was extracted at low temperatures, which helps preserve the antioxidants. Look for cold-pressed avocado oil as well. In the *Best Oils for Cooking and Salads* cheat sheet, I share tips for buying and storing oils.

Nuts and seeds are another healthy fats category. They contain a combination of omega-3 and omega-6 fatty acids. Almonds, hemp, and pumpkin seeds are higher in protein. Chia and flaxseeds are higher in fiber. Flaxseeds have more omega-3, almonds have more monounsaturated fatty acids, and walnuts have more omega-6 fatty acids. What to make out of this information? Include a variety in your diet!

While flaxseeds in meals and snacks add some fiber, skip flaxseed oil. It doesn't have the active beneficial EPA and DHA omega-3 fatty acids. It goes bad very quickly, and if you consume it after it's gone rancid, free radicals can develop in your body. If you choose to use flaxseed oil, buy a small container, store it in your fridge, and finish it quickly.

It's very easy to overeat fats so watch your portions. In my balanced plate graph, fat is a condiment. But an important one! At meals or snacks, eat two tablespoons of nuts and seeds, a quarter of an avocado, or two teaspoons oil per serving. In recipes, I use 1–2 tablespoons oils since most recipes yield at least 4 servings. If you use cheese or dairy, limit your portion to ¼ cup cheese, a cup of whole milk, or 2 teaspoons butter.

LOSING WEIGHT

Will you lose weight eating these recipes?

There are many factors that contribute to your ability to lose weight. We are all genetically different, and our genes interact with our environment in a complex way. Your metabolism may be less efficient if you have a history of yoyo dieting, several cycles of weight loss and weight regain, and restrictive eating.

The body resists changes and prefers stability. Your body is going to hold on to the weight you have on to maintain homeostasis. It feels comfortable and safe from famine. The longer you've had the weight on you, the more difficult it will be to lose it. Getting back to your weight from 20 years ago is more difficult than getting back to your weight from 2 years ago.

You will burn more calories if you are:
- A man: due to hormones and more muscle mass than women
- Leaner: muscles burn more calories than fat
- Younger: hormones slow down metabolism and we lose muscle mass as we age
- More active: exercise uses up energy
- Heavier: more cells in your body

means you need more energy to feed them

- Sick or in recovery: the body needs energy to fight microbes, heal, and repair tissues

Don't let these factors discourage you though. You can't change the past or your genes or your gender. And you can't stop time for sure. But you can focus on today and improve for tomorrow. You will learn a lot about food as you practice planning and cooking meals in my balance and detox framework. You will learn a lot about yourself and your current habits too.

The recipes in *The Detox Way* average about 400 calories per meals. Breakfast recipes are lighter, and snack recipes are around 200 calories. If you eat three meals and two snacks a day, you'll end up with 1600 calories a day. This will help 'lightly active' women who are in a healthy weight or slightly overweight and between the ages 30 to 50 years old maintain their weight. Light activity is defined as light exercise or sports 3–5 days a week.

If you are a woman between 30 and 50 years and want to lose weight, drop one snack from your day and step up your exercise. You can do that by adding another exercise session to your week or increasing the intensity of your current activity. You can try to make the meals smaller, but don't undereat because that will backfire.

If you're a man or a woman who is more active and want to maintain your weight, you might need a little bit more food. This means the recipes will yield fewer servings. Or, you could double some recipes so you have enough leftovers.

In *The Detox Way*, I don't focus on calories. It's not a weight loss cookbook and I don't want you to obsess about the numbers. I calculated many of the meals and the combinations I suggest to make sure they are balanced and within the calorie range.

The meals are high in protein, which will help you lose weight. Recipes that are 3-in-1, such as main dish salads or casseroles, will be about 20–30% protein. Vegetable and starch recipes will need to be paired with a protein dish like chicken or salmon. Snacks will have about 5–15 grams protein.

There are times when tracking the amount of food you eat is a good idea. If you already select healthy foods yet can't lose weight, tracking will help you uncover slip-ups. Are you overeating healthy foods like avocado or nuts? Are your meals low in protein? Are you undereating? Are you not consistent? Do you drinks calorie-dense beverages without noticing? Do you snack too often? And so forth.

It's well agreed on that keeping a food journal and tracking how much you eat improve the odds of losing weight. It's a combination of accountability and knowledge about your food and your habits. Give it a try if it doesn't make you stressed or anxious.

If you do track your food, use Apps because they are more informative than just listing foods on a piece of paper. Check out My Fitness Pal or Lose It. They have a wide selection of foods to choose from. You can add custom foods, create recipes, and scan the barcode of products for easy and faster use. Add your favorite recipes from *The Detox Way* to your App.

Tracking your food is also helpful if you exercise regularly and still can't lose weight. We often overestimate our exercise and the number of calories we burn, while we underestimate how much we eat. We eat more after a good workout because we 'deserve' it or because we think our activity was intense enough and long enough to burn an extra dessert. And often, this is not the case.

Sometimes it's physiology and hormones. People report feeling more hungry on days they work out. This is possible due to changes in hunger and satiety hormones and blood sugar fluctuations. To avoid excessive hunger, eat a balanced meal or snack that contains carbohydrates and proteins within 1 hour of intense exercise. Plan your day so that you eat lunch or dinner after your workout so you don't need an additional snack.

And rest, rest, rest! Physical and mental

stress increases your appetite. Give yourself some time to de-stress and reboot. What relaxes you the most? Exercise helps reduce mental and emotional stress, just make sure you budget some recovery time.

Sleep deprivation, even for one night, will make you have a bigger appetite and more carbohydrate cravings. It also reduces the levels of satiety hormones, so the amount of food that typically makes you satisfied doesn't feel enough. It's recommended to get 7–8 hours of restful sleep on regular basis.

And finally, don't get caught up with your weight. Sometimes shifting your focus from the number on the scale to your energy level and how you feel helps the weight come off naturally. Eating fresh, nutrient-rich, and detox-boosting foods will give you more energy so you can be more active. You'll feel uplifted and less dragged down, which will motivate you to seek other healthy lifestyle changes. And the delicious recipes you have will make planning and cooking at home more consistent.

If you're struggling with your weight, my guess is that you have crash-dieted in the past. Let's do things differently here. Let's get comfortable cooking healthy meals. Let's learn how to plan and prepare easy recipes. Let's enjoy detox wholesome foods. I did my best to give you tools to help you do all that.

WATER

Water is the lifeline of your body. It makes up 60–75% of your body. Your brain, lungs, kidneys, muscles, and blood are made of almost 90% water.

Water has many roles and functions. It keeps membranes moist, helps manufacture hormones and neurotransmitters, regulates body temperature, allows your cells to grow and reproduce, forms saliva, converts food to energy, delivers oxygen and nutrients to your cells, and lubricates joints. Water promotes healthy elastic skin and reduces wrinkles.

In terms of detoxification, water flushes waste out of your body through urine. This is important because you want all those toxins your liver just neutralized to exit. If you don't have enough water in your body, your kidneys will adjust and reduce urine production, keeping these toxins stuck inside.

Many people are walking around dehydrated. Here are some red flags that your body isn't getting enough water:
- Feeling thirsty often. Your body is already mildly dehydrated by the time you start to notice thirst.
- Dry skin and excessive wrinkles. Feeling that your skin looks older than you actually are
- Reduced cognitive and physical performance

- Lack of focus
- Constant headaches
- Brain fog
- Fatigue
- Bad mood
- Constipation

There isn't a set recommendation for water across the board. It depends on your weight, physical activity, outside temperature, and the amount of food you eat. The Institute of Medicine recommends 13 cups of fluids for men and 9 cups of fluids for women a day. A widely spread recommendation is to drink half an ounce to one ounce of water for each pound you weight. If you weigh 140 pounds, you would need 70 to 140 ounces of water a day.

Because many factors affect hydration, it's best to be in tuned with your own body needs. Monitoring your urine color is a good personal indicator. It needs to be pale and barely yellow. Anything darker than that can indicate early signs of dehydration. If you have any of the symptoms above despite drinking water regularly, try adding 2 to 4 more cups and see if that makes a difference.

Keep in mind that you can get fluids from other sources too. Watery vegetables and fruits like cucumber, lettuce, bell pepper, orange, watermelon, and many others provide your body with water. Soups and stews help you load on fluids. Beverages like coconut water, dairy or non-dairy milks, smoothies, and freshly squeezed juices improve hydration. Just try to limit excessive juices, especially commercial varieties, because they're loaded with added sugars.

Some people believe that coffee and tea are dehydrating, but it's a myth that has been debunked. While they can have a diuretic effect, it doesn't offset the hydration they offer or the amount of fluid you get in when you drink them. Don't count on them as the sole source of water of course.

If you don't like the taste of water, you can try a few things. Squeeze some lemon or lime juice in your water. Add cucumber, strawberry, or orange slices. Mix an ounce of non-sweetened cranberry, tart cherry, or pomegranate juices with 8 ounces of water.

You can also have a glass of sparkling water. Try warm water with shredded ginger root in cold weather.

There are ways to remind yourself to drink water if forgetting, or being distracted, is your challenge. These are some tricks that helped my patients, and hopefully some are good ideas for you to try:

- Always carry a reusable water bottle that's at least 24 ounces. If you prefer plastic, make sure it's PBA free and don't put it in the dishwasher
- Leave a reusable water bottle at work or large glass and fill it up from the cooler or the water fountain first thing in the morning
- Set an alarm every 3 hours and drink 2 cups of water when the alarm goes off
- Leave a water bottle or large cup within an arm's reach and sip regularly
- Every morning, place 4 16-ounce plastic bottles visible on the kitchen counter. They must be gone by bedtime (see my note about plastic bottles though)
- Leave at least a 16-ounce bottle or a large glass of water next to your bed and drink first thing in the morning
- Drink 20 minutes before grabbing food anytime you feel hungry

The type of water you drink makes a difference. Let's take a look at some of the options.

Research from the Environmental Working Group indicate that tap water is contaminated with over 300 chemicals. These include volatile organic chemicals (VOCs), herbicides, pesticides, heavy metals, endocrine disrupters, chloride, fluoride, parasite, bacteria, and potentially others.

Fluoride is a controversial topic that I will briefly touch on. It competes with iodine, which is needed for proper thyroid health, less available for your thyroid gland. If there's a benefit to fluoride for dental health, it may be enough to have it in your toothpaste, but not necessarily in your water.

Plastic water bottles contain plastics and other synthetic compounds that leach into the water. Often, bottled water is not very different from tap water, just more expensive and increases the load of plastic waste on earth! Don't count on them for regular use. Store few bottles in the fridge or a cool place for those last minute runs out the door. Toss bottles that have been exposed to heat. Don't reuse them.

Spring and mineral water bottles are superior to filtered water bottles. These usually come from a natural underground spring source and contain healthy minerals and trace elements. Minerals are important for many functions in your body. They are often more pricy than filtered water bottles.

Better than bottled water, consider an in-home filtration system. Standard pitcher filters, like Brita, are a good starting point. They use granulated activated charcoal to remove some contaminants. They remove chlorine and improve the taste of water, but they will not remove VOCs, heavy metals, or fluorine. Faucet mounted filters use the same technology as pitcher filters.

There are advanced filtration options if you're willing to make an investment. Solid block carbon filters remove herbicides, pesticides, VOCs, chemicals, bacteria, parasites, fluoride (with filter attachment), chloride, heavy metals, nitrate, and nitrites. They don't filter out minerals, which is a good thing. While they cost more upfront, they will save you money on filters on the long run because you won't need to replace the filters as often.

The downside of having a solid block carbon filter is that it takes up space on your counter top. You also have to fill it up with water manually.

There are many other water filtration technologies on the market. Some of the options include ion exchange, multistage filtration, reverse osmosis, whole house filtration, and few other options. Do some research to decide on the best option for you.

Remember that any filter is better than no filter. Don't let anxiety about the best type or the cost of high-end products deter you from filtering your drinking water at all.

Balance Cheat Sheets

The next few pages are helpful cheat sheets that I use often with my patients. Print these pages and keep them handy in your kitchen for a quick reference. They also help you come up with meal and snack ideas and guide you if you want to make substitutions.

Here's a list of the cheat sheets:
- Non-Starchy Vegetables
- Healthy Carbohydrates
- Understanding Carbohydrate Numbers in Labels
- Healthy Proteins
- Healthy Fats
- Best Oils for Salads and Cooking
- Healthy Salad Builder
- Healthy Smoothie Builder
- Healthy Snack Builder

Non-Starchy Vegetables

Green

- Arugula
- Asparagus
- Beet greens
- Bell pepper, green
- Bok choy
- Broccoli
- Brussels sprouts
- Cabbage, green
- Celery
- Cilantro
- Collard greens
- Cucumber
- Dandelion greens
- Endive lettuce
- Green beans
- Green onions
- Jalapeño peppers
- Kale
- Lettuce
- Mustard greens
- Okra
- Parsley
- Pea sprouts
- Snow peas
- Spinach
- Sugar snap peas
- Watercress
- Zucchini

Red

- Bell pepper, red
- Red onion
- Red rhubarb
- Tomato, fresh *(tomato paste and pasta sauce are concentrated in sugar. Count as a carbohydrate)*

Yellow/Orange

- Bell peppers, yellow and orange
- Carrots *(if eating more than 1 cup, count as a carbohydrate)*
- Summer squash
- Tomato, yellow

White

- Artichoke hearts
- Bamboo shoots
- Bean sprouts
- Cabbage
- Cauliflower
- Fennel (bulb)
- Garlic
- Ginger
- Hearts of palm
- Kohlrabi
- Leek
- Mushroom
- Onion
- Shallot

Purple/Blue

- Asparagus, purple
- Cabbage, purple
- Eggplant
- Carrots, purple

Notes

- Eat 50% raw and 50% cooked.
- Include many colors for more antioxidants and a better looking plate!
- Choose fresh and seasonal when possible. If not, frozen vegetables without seasonings or sauces are a good and convenient option.
- **For salads:** pick from lettuce, spinach, kale, arugula, cabbage (Cole slaw mix), pea sprouts, parsley, basil, fennel, mushroom, grape tomatoes, shredded Brussels sprouts, and shredded carrots.
- **For smoothies and juices:** pick from spinach, kale, cucumber, carrots, celery, and ginger.

Aim for
2 cups at meals
1 cup at snacks

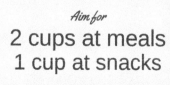

Healthy Carbohydrates

Starchy Vegetables

- 1 cup cooked spaghetti or acorn squash
- 1 cup beet root
- 1 cup carrot
- 1 cup pumpkin
- 1/2 cup butternut squash
- 1/2 cup parsnip
- 1/2 cup Jerusalem artichoke
- 1/2 medium white or sweet potato (about 1/2 cup)

Grains (if tolerated)

- 1/3 cup cooked brown/wild rice
- 1/3 cup cooked quinoa
- 1/2 cup cooked oatmeal, buckwheat, kasha
- 1/3 cup of cooked teff or millet
- Corn (1/2 cup of kernel, 1/2 corn on the cob, 1/3 cup of polenta, 2 1/2 cup popcorn), choose organic corn because regular corn is genetically modified.

Low Glycemic Load Fruit

- 1 small apple, pear, orange, nectarine, peach
- 1 cup berries, grapes, melons, papaya, pienapple
- 1 large kiwi
- 2 fresh plums, tangerines, clementines, apricots
- 1/2 grapefruit
- 1/2 cup pasta sauce

High Glycemic Load Fruit

Choose less frequently:
- 3/4 cup apple sauce (no sugar)
- 1 small banana
- 2 tablespoons raisins, cranberries, dried bananas
- 3 prunes, 3 dried apricots, 3 dried figs, 2 small dates

Dairy* (if tolerated)

- 1 cup milk
- 1 cup plain regular or Greek yogurt

 Also contain 8 grams protein per serving

Legumes (if tolerated)

- 1/2 cup cooked beans (kidney, black, pinto)
- 1/2 cup cooked peas (green peas, chickpeas, split peas)
- 1/2 cup cooked lentils (any color)

 Also contain 4-9 grams protein per serving

Aim for:

- 2 servings at meals (about 30 grams carbohydrates)
- 1 serving at snacks (about 15 grams carbohydrates)
- Each serving above contains about 15 grams carbohydrates

Notes

- Non-starchy veggies (like broccoli, green beans, kale, etc) contain a small amount of carbs. Don't worry about it though. They are fiber-packed and good for you!
- Not listed here are pastas, breads, crackers, cookies, pastries, etc. They have zero nutrition and too many carbs. Limit, and choose healthy options instead.
- Many foods contain hidden sugars and carbs. Read labels to make sure you stick to recommended limit.

Understanding Carbohydrates Numbers In Labels

Each serving of carbohydrates is about 15 grams. Use this guide when you buy smoothies, juices, snack bars, or when assessing the nutrition content of restaurant meals.

While it's important to reduce sugars, the **TOTAL CARBOHYDRATE** content is what matters for balancing meals, managing blood sugar, and reducing cravings. Foods like bread, pasta, rice, and beans low in sugar but high in total carbohydrates. They may look good if you look at sugars only, but their carbohydrate load can be heavy. Non-starchy veggies (like broccoli, green beans, kale, etc) contain a small amount of carbs. Don't worry about it though. They are fiber-packed and good for you!

Aim for:

2 carbohydrate servings at meals
(30- g total carbohydrates)

1 carbohydrate serving at snacks
(15-30 g total carbohydrates)

1. Check the serving size

2. Check total carbohydrate grams

3. If 15 grams carbohydrates are about 1 serving, then in this example, 37 grams of total carbohydrates are 2.5 servings carbohydrates

4. Then 1 serving of this food, which is 2/3 cups, is going to count as 2.5 servings carbohydrates

Nutrition Facts

Serving Size 2/3 cup (55g)
Servings Per Container About 8

Amount Per Serving

Calories 230   Calories from Fat 40

	% Daily Value*
Total Fat 8g	**12%**
Saturated Fat 1g	**5%**
Trans Fat 0g	
Cholesterol 0mg	**0%**
Sodium 160mg	**7%**
Total Carbohydrate 37g	**12%**
Dietary Fiber 4g	**16%**
Sugars 1g	
Protein 3g	

Vitamin A	10%
Vitamin C	8%
Calcium	20%
Iron	45%

* Percent Daily Values are based on a 2,000 calorie diet. Your daily value may be higher or lower depending on your calorie needs.

		Calories:	2,000	2,500
Total Fat	Less than		65g	80g
Sat Fat	Less than		20g	25g
Cholesterol	Less than		300mg	300mg
Sodium	Less than		2,400mg	2,400mg
Total Carbohydrate			300g	375g
Dietary Fiber			25g	30g

Healthy Proteins

Animal-Based

Plant-Based

Seafood

Fish: cod, flounder, haddock, halibut, salmon, sardine, tilapia, tuna, trout, catfish

Shellfish: shrimp, oyster, crab, lobster, clam, scallop

Grilled, broiled, baked, simmered, poached

★ 4 ounces: 28 g protein ★

Poultry

Chicken: breast, thigh, drumstick, whole chicken

Cornish hen

Turkey

Lean ground chicken or turkey

★ 4 ounces: 28 g protein ★

Beans

1/2 cup beans (black, kidney, garbanzo, white): 7 g protein

1/2 cup lentils: 9 g protein

1/2 cup green peas: 4.5 g protein

1/3 hummus: 6 g protein

Beans also have 15 g carbs in a serving

Non-Starchy Vegetables

- **Spinach**
- **Asparagus**
- **Broccoli**

★ 1 cup cooked has 2-5 g protein ★

Red Meat/Organs

Beef, trimmed of fat: Roast, New York strip, sirloin, tenderloin, 90-95% lean ground

Lamb: chop, leg, roast

Pork: tenderloin, roast, lean chop veal

Organs: heart, kidney, liver

★ 4 ounces; 28 g protein ★

Eggs

1 Large egg: 6 g protein

1 extra-large egg: 7 g protein

1 egg white: 4 g protein

Nuts

1/4 cup nuts (almond, walnut, cashew, peanut, pistachio): 5-8 g protein

2 tablespoons nut butter: 5-8 g protein

1 tablespoon seeds (sunflower, pumpkin, sesame, chia seed, hemp, flax): 1-3 g protein

Grains

1/3 cup quinoa: 3 g protein

1/3 cup brown rice: 2 g protein

1/2 cup steel-cut or rolled oats: 3 g protein

1/2 cup rolled kasha (buckwheat) 3 g protein

★ Grains are high in carbs. Not a main protein source ★

Protein Powders

Beef gelatin protein powder
Egg white protein powder
Whey protein powder

Buy our recommended products at www.nourzibdeh.com/shop

★ Choose unflavored and read label for specific protein content ★

Dairy

1 cup milk: 8 g protein

1 cup plain yogurt: 11 g protein

1/2 cup plain Greek yogurt: 12 g protein

Protein Powders

Pea protein powder
Hemp protein powder
Rice protein powder

Buy our recommended products at www.nourzibdeh.com/shop

★ Choose unflavored and read label for specific protein contrnt ★

Aim for...

20-30 g at meals
10-15 g at snacks

Healthy Fats

One serving is about 100 calories and 9 grams fat. Aim for 1-2 servings at meals and 1 serving at snacks. Aim for a total of 6-7 servings a day, depending on your activity level and the amount of carbs/protein in your diet. Individualized recommendation is better if you're trying to lose weight.

One Serving is:
- 2 tablespoons nuts like almond, cashew, hazelnut, macadamia nut, walnut, pecan, Brazil nut, pine nuts
- 1 tablespoon nut or seed butter like almond, cashew, sunflower, tahini paste
- 1/4 avocado
- 8 green or kalamata olives
- 2 teaspoons olive, avocado, or coconut oil (see options to the right)
- 1/3 cup shredded unsweetened coconut
- ¼ cup canned coconut milk

If incorporating dairy:
- 1 slice cheese
- 2 teaspoons grass-fed butter or ghee
- 1 cup whole milk

High Cooking Temperature

Avocado oil, cold-pressed

Coconut oil, cold-pressed

Ghee, from grass-fed cows

Low Cooking Temperature and baking below 400 F

Avocado oil, cold-pressed

Unrefined coconut oil, cold-pressed

Extra virgin olive oil, cold-pressed

Ghee and butter from grass-fed cows

Salads and Dips (no heat)

Extra virgin olive oil, cold-pressed

Flaxseed oil, cold-pressed

Avocado oil, cold-pressed

Best Oils for Cooking and Salads

Medium-low heat / baking at lower than 375 F

Cooking at a lower temperature preserves nutrient content and prevents toxic compounds from developing. Choose from:

- **Avocado oil**, cold-pressed. High smoke point and flavorless.
- **Extra-virgin olive oil,** cold-pressed. Okay to use for quick low-heat saute, as long as it doesn't smoke.
- **Unrefined coconut oil,** great for baking, roasting, sauteing. Has a noticable coconut flavor.
- **Ghee and butter from grass-fed cows,** look for 'grass-fed' claim on the label. Don't let it smoke.
- **Unrefined toasted sesame oil,** strong flavor, great with Asian dishes. Use sparingly due to high omega-6 content.

Deep frying / baking at higher than 375 F

Avoid frying and high-heat cooking in general because they cause compounds that promote cancers to develop. If needed on occasional basis, choose from:

- **Avocado oil**, cold-pressed. High smoke point and flavorless.
- **Coconut oil, refined* or unrefined**, the check the label for the specific product smoke point
- **Ghee (clarified butter)**, look for 'grass-fed' claim on the label. Don't let it smoke.
- **Organic, cold-pressed, refined* sunflower, safflower, or sesame oil.** Use sparingly due to high omega-6 content.

*read about refining below

Salads and dips (no heat)

These 3 oils are the most superior nutritionally.

- **Extra-virgin olive oil**, cold-pressed. Consider drizzling on vegetables AFTER steaming or roasting to preserve antioxidant content
- **Avocado oil**, cold-pressed.
- **Flaxseed oil**, cold-pressed. Contains omega-3 fatty acids. Must store in the fridge. Only use for salads and never for cooking. Buy a small amount and use fast.

Buying and Storing

- Buy oils in dark glass containers in small quantity.
- Store away from heat. Keep in a dark cool area like a pantry or bottom cabinet (heat goes up).
- Check expiration dates and toss any remaining oil beyond that date. Flaxseed oil goes bad quickly.
- Smell the oil. If different than how it smelled when you first bought it, it's likely rancid. Some oils, like unrefined coconut and sesame, have a natural strong smell.

Avoid Completely

- Vegetable oils (corn, soy, canola, cotton, etc). Heavily processed and high in omega-6 (inflammatory)
- Margarine
- Fake/imitation butters and spreads
- Trans fats (partially hydrogenated fats). Read labels

Terms to Understand

Extra-virgin: the first press of the olives. Best quality and taste.

Expeller-pressed: pressed mechanically without chemicals.

Cold-pressed: pressed in controlled cool temperature. All cold-pressed oils are expeller-pressed.

Unrefined: minimal straining. The oil contains some solids and has strong flavor. Best for low heat.

Refined: solids removed. Conventional refining uses high heat and harsh chemicals. Natural refining uses mechanical straining and recommended over chemicals. Refined oils tolerate heat better than unrefined.

Smoke point: the temperature at which the oil start to smoke and develop harmful compounds.

Omega-6 fatty acids: poly-unsaturated fats that are inflammatory in excess, especially with low omega-3 intake. Reduce omega-6 intake in your diet.

Healthy Salad Builder

 1 Non-starchy veggies (at least 2 cups)

Start with salad greens

Lettuce, spinach, kale, arugula, basil, parsley, cilantro. Darker greens are more nutritious.

Top with:

Tomatoes (grape tomatoes for convenience), bell peppers, celery, white or purple cabbage (use coleslaw mix for convenience), cucumber, mushroom, carrots (buy shredded for convenience), broccoli, cauliflower, artichoke hearts (from a jar). The more variety and color the better.

 2 Protein (choose one)

- Grilled or shredded leftover cooked chicken (4 ounces)
- Grilled or baked fish (salmon, cod, tilapia, tuna), shrimp, or scallop (4 ounces)
- Lean cut of steak (4 ounces)
- Lean ground beef, chicken, or turkey (4 ounces)
- 2 hard-boiled eggs
- 1 cup cooked beans (black, pinto, kidney, chickpea, lentil) + 1/4 cup cheese
- 1 cup cooked beans (black, pinto, kidney, chickpea, lentil) + 1/4 cup nuts or seeds

 3 Carbs (choose one)

*(If you selected beans for your proteins, **skip the carbs here**)*

- 1/2 cup cooked beans (black, pinto, kidney, chickpea, lentil)
- 1 cup cut-up fresh fruit (strawberries, blueberries, peach, apple, pear, mandarines)
- 1/4 cup dried fruit (raisins, cranberries)
- 1/2 cup cooked quinoa
- 1 piece of fruit on the side like an apple, pear, or orange

 4 Fats (choose two)

*(If you selected cheese, nuts, or seeds as your proteins, choose only **one** fat here)*

- 1 teaspoon extra-virgin olive oil
- 2 tablespoons olives
- 1/4 avocado or 1/4 cup guacamole
- 1 tablespoon olive oil-based dressing
- 2 tablespoons nuts or seeds
- 2 tablespoons cheese

BASIC SALAD DRESSING

- ¼ cup extra-version olive oil
- 2 tablespoon balsamic vinegar
- juice of 1 lemon
- ¼ teaspoon mustard
- ¼ teaspoon salt
- ¼ teaspoon ground black pepper
- ½ teaspoon dried oregano

Combine in a glass jar and shake. Store in the fridge for up to 2 weeks.

Healthy *Smoothie* Builder

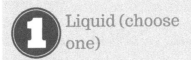 **Liquid (choose one)**

- 1 cup water
- 1 cup coconut water
- 1 cup 2% milk (if tolerated)
- 1 cup non-dairy milk like almond, coconut, or hemp
- 1/2 cup water + 1/2 cup 100% juice like pomegranate, cranberry, grape, or orange

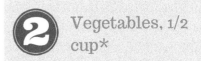 **Vegetables, 1/2 cup***

- Baby spinach
- Baby kale
- Carrots
- Beets
- Cucumber
- Mint
- Basil

Start with a handful. If you enjoy the taste, increase amount to 1 cup

 Fruit, 1.5 cups total

Choose 1-3 different fruits, for a total of 1.5 cups max to keep sugar low.

- Berries (blueberry, strawberry, raspberry, blackberry)
- Mango / pineapple
- Peach
- Banana
- Apple / pear
- Kiwi
- Cherries
- Orange

 Protein (choose one option)

- 1/2 cup plain Greek yogurt
- 2 tablespoons almond butter
- 3 tablespoons hemp seeds
- 1/3 cup chia seeds
- Protein powder to provide 18-24 grams protein (see notes in next box)

If you used dairy milk in step 1, that will add 8 grams of protein to your smoothie

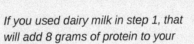

Protein Powders Notes

- Choose unflavored products. They contain fewer or no artificial ingredients, sweeteners, fillers, etc.
- Try one of these: collagen protein, pea, hemp, egg white, or undenatured whey (if you tolerate dairy)
- For my top quality picks, go to www.nourzibdeh.com/shop

 Fat* (choose one)

- 1/4 avocado
- 1 tablespoon peanut or almond butter
- 1 tablespoon flax seeds or chia seeds
- 1 teaspoon coconut or fish oil
- 2 tablespoons canned coconut milk

Skip this step if you used nuts or seeds as your protein.

 Extra Flavors

- Detoxification: 1/2 inch cube ginger, 1/4 cup packed fresh cilantro or parsley, or 1 tablespoon lemon or lime juice
- Sweeteners: 1 teaspoon raw honey, 1 teaspoon 100% maple syrup, 1 date, or stevia
- Others: cinnamon, cacao nibs, cocoa powder, maca powder, green tea powder, almond extract, vanilla extract

General Notes

- Blend greens with liquid first until chopped and smooth
- Have fun experimenting!
- Drink smoothie immediately. If not, store in the fridge for no more than one day in an air-tight container
- If you have diarrhea, gas, or bloating, you will need to modify the types of liquid, fruit, and fats. Contact us for help.

Healthy Snack Builder

 Vegetables

Choose at least 1 cup:

- Cucumber sticks
- Bell pepper sticks
- Celery sticks
- Cherry tomatoes
- Salsa
- Romaine lettuce (baby leaves from the inside are delicious)
- Broccoli florets
- Cauliflower florets
- Radish
- Snow peas
- Sugar snap peas
- Nori wraps
- Carrot sticks (1/2 cup max and combine with other vegetables. Carrots have a higher sugar content than the other vegetables listed)

 Great source of fiber and water

 Carbohydrate

Choose one option (fruit is always healthier than crackers or breads) :

- 1 small apple, pear, peach or orange
- 1 cup berries, melons, pineapple, or grapes
- 1/2 banana
- 2 clementines, plums, or kiwi
- 2 dried figs or small dates
- 1/4 cup raisins or cranberries
- 1/2 cup unsweetened applesauce
- 1/4 cup shrimp cocktail sauce
- 8 Blue Diamond Almond Thins
- 10 tortilla chips
- 2 thin rice cakes
- 4 small crackers*
- 1 small toast*
- 1/2 English muffin or pita*

---

* Contain gluten. Choose gluten-free alternatives if necessary

 Each option contains about 15 g carbohydrates

3 **Protein/Fat**

Choose one option:

- 2 tablespoons almonds, peanuts, pistachio, pumpkin seeds, walnuts, or shredded unsweetened coconut
- 2 tablespoons almond or peanut butter
- 1 hard-boiled egg
- 1/4 avocado
- 1/3 cup guacamole
- 1/3 cup hummus or roasted chickpeas
- 2 ounces turkey, chicken, roast beef, or smoked salmon*
- 10 cocktail shrimp
- 1 slice cheese like cheddar, Swiss, provolone
- 1 string cheese
- 2 small Cabot individual cheddar
- 1/2 cup plain or Greek yogurt, kefir, or cottage cheese

---

* Choose nitrate and preservative-free deli meat. Check out Applegate products

Each option contains 5-15 g protein (except for avocado)

Examples from the lists above

- Celery sticks + 1 sliced apple dipped in 2 tablespoons almond butter
- Broccoli and cauliflower florets + 2 clementines + 1 string cheese
- Salsa + bell pepper sticks + 10 tortilla chips + 1/4 cup guacamole
- Trail mix: 1/4 cup raisins + 1 tablespoon shredded coconut + 1 tablespoon pumpkin seeds
- 1/4 cup cocktail sauce + 10 cocktail shrimp
- 1 cup celery and cucumber + 1 hard-boiled egg + 1 small apple
- 1/2 cup blueberries + chia seed pudding (recipe in www.nourzibdeh.com/TheDetoxWay)

Snack bars, drinks, and others:

ONE item from this list can be your snack. Aim for 10 grams protein and 3 grams fiber, and stick to 200 calories. Add vegetables on the side for more filling snack.

- **Bars**: try LARABAR (cashew cookie, peanut butter chocolate, or peanut butter cookie), RXBAR (any flavor), Pure Organic Fruit & Nut Bars (any flavor), EVO Hemp bars (any flavor)
- **Drinks**:12-ounce unsweetened or vanilla latte made with non-fat, 2%, or coconut milk, 12 or 16-ounce cappuccino made with non-fat, 2%, or coconut milk, 12-ounce
- If you drink coffee, tea, and herbal teas, no more than 3 teaspoons of sugar a day. Better to cut completely.

Healthy Snack List

This is a list of healthy snacks you can choose from. A high-protein snack that also contains non-starchy vegetables will keep you satisfied for longer. In general, aim for 10 grams of protein and 3-5 grams of fiber, and no more than to 200 calories in your snack.

- 1 tablespoon almond butter dipped with celery and an apple or pear
- 1 tablespoon almond butter spread over a rice cake
- 1 cup of fresh berries with 10 almonds
- ¼ cup dried fruit with 10 almonds
- 1 hard-boiled egg with cut up vegetables and small fruit
- 1 cup of baby carrots, cucumber, celery, and pepper sticks with guacamole
- 1 cup of baby carrots, cucumber, celery, and pepper sticks with hummus
- 1 cup unsweetened coconut water with one hard-boiled egg
- 1 cup unsweetened coconut or almond milk with 1/2 cup fresh fruit
- Shredded vegetables and leftover chicken or shrimp wrapped in seaweed
- 8 olives, cucumber sticks, and 1 cup of grapes
- 8 olives and smoked salmon on top of cucumber rings
- 2 ounces smoked salmon and fresh vegetables or roasted (leftovers or jarred roasted peppers)
- 8 cocktail shrimp with 1 tablespoon of cocktail sauce
- 1 cup berries or apple slices topped with 2 tablespoons unsweetened coconut flakes, flax meal, or chopped pecans
- Mini smoothie (half a portion from the recipes in the The Detox Way cookbook)
- 1 bowl of bone broth
- 1 cup of green tea with 1 date and 10 almonds
- 12-ounce coconut milk latte. Sprinkle cinnamon or chocolate powder for more flavor
- Bars: try LARABAR (cashew cookie, peanut butter chocolate, or peanut butter cookie), RXBAR (any flavor), Pure Organic Fruit & Nut Bars (any flavor), EVO Hemp bars (any flavor). Ideally, choose bars with 10 grams of protein or more

If you tolerate dairy, you can try:

- 1/2 cup plain regular or Greek yogurt with 1/2 cup fresh fruit, topped with 1 tablespoon chia seeds (or other nuts)
- 1/2 cup cottage cheese with cucumber and carrot slices
- 1 ounce of cheese (about 1 slice or 1 stick) with cut up vegetables
- 1 cup 2% milk with 1/2 cup fresh fruit
- 12-ounce low fat plain latte. Sprinkle cinnamon or chocolate powder for more flavor

DETOX WITH FOOD

WHAT DETOX MEANS AND WHY IT MATTERS

A clean wholesome way of eating is the corner stone of my counseling and nutrition therapy. There's no clear definition of what a 'clean' food is.

My interpretation of a clean food is a food that contains no chemicals, preservatives, pesticides, or genetic modification. It's not processed or very minimally processed at most. It's an apple, a carrot, steel-cut or rolled oats, grass-fed meat, raw honey, etc. It's not fruit roll-ups, or veggie chips, or sweetened breakfast cereal, or processed hot dogs, or fish sticks, or high-fructose corn syrup.

A clean food often doesn't have a label or ingredients list. And when it does, the list contains only a few ingredients that you can recognize and easily spell.

Clean real foods are packed with nutrients that help your body detox. They don't overload your liver's job of clearing out toxins and any unknown ingredients.

Detox sounds like a crazy trend or fad, but it's not. Your liver has been detoxing since the day you were born. But as the years go by, you (and me) accumulate toxins from many different sources through our food and environment. Take a look at this list of these things your liver has to process:

- Pesticides and herbicides in food
- Rancid oils and free radicals
- Preservatives, food colorings, artificial sweeteners and artificial flavors
- Chloride, fluoride, and bromide in water
- Plastics
- Polyphenols (like BPA and others): found in dental sealants, white composite dental fillings, water bottles, sports equipment, the lining of water pipes, the lining of food cans, and sales receipts
- Organic pollutants
- Car fumes
- Cigarette smoking and second-hand smoke
- Prescription and over-the-counter medications
- Alcohol
- Recreational drugs
- Chemicals from hobbies like painting
- Chemicals from house renovation projects (carpet, paint, treated wood floors, treated furniture)
- Lawn and backyard treatments
- Make up and beauty products
- Cleaning products
- Microbes, pathogens and their toxins

Some of us are better at detoxing than others. Your genetic make-up contributes 15% of how well you clear waste. Diet and lifestyle contribute 85%! That's a whole lot! And that means you CAN and HAVE to do something about it.

If you have 2 or more of these complaints, then a bottleneck in your detoxification system may be the blame:
- Sluggish, tired, fatigued
- Brain fog, difficulty focusing
- Depression
- Restless or hyperactive
- Anxiety, irritability, mood swings
- Insomnia, trouble falling back to sleep
- Weight gain or difficulty losing weight
- Muscle and joint aches
- Fibromyalgia
- Headaches
- Skin issues like eczema, acne, psoriasis
- Dependent on sweets, carbs, and/or coffee for energy
- Intense sugar and other cravings
- Bloating and water retention
- Post nasal drip, frequent need to clear throat

What you eat, digest, and absorb will ultimately affect your detoxification pathways.

There are two main pathways involved in detoxification in the liver; phase 1 and phase 2. These two phases work together to help your clear out compounds that are foreign and harmful. Each phase needs specific nutrients to progress efficiently.

In a nutshell, your liver will take a certain compound and walk it through pathways of phases. Nutrients like vitamins C, E, B_2, B_3, B_6, B_{12}, and folate, as well as glutathione and flavonoids are needed for phase 1 to happen optimally. Interesting, an initial toxic compounds will exit phase 1 even more toxic. At that point, it's called a detox intermediate.

What happens next is very important. Enzymes in phase 2 take this intermediate and process it further until it's a safe compound that dissolves in water. At that point, it will be excreted in the urine, bowel movements, or sweat.

Phase 2 is very important because without it, your body will be stuck with intermediates that are more toxic than what you started out with. Nutrients that boost that phase include amino acids from protein foods and sulfur from foods like onion, garlic, and cruciferous vegetables. In addition, it needs magnesium, vitamin C, vitamin B_5, vitamin B_{12}, folic acid, choline, glutathione (antioxidant), and few others.

In the next section, I talk about each one of these food components. You don't need to worry about the science. It's there for you if you like to read it. If you look at the recipes in *The Detox Way*, you will clearly see that they are packed with foods are rich in these nutrients. I read the research and did the work for you. All you have to do next is cook and enjoy it!

Eating the detox way doesn't have to be restrictive. You don't have to do juice cleanses or drink lemon water and cayenne pepper all day long. In fact, these types of cleanses will hurt you because they deprive your body from important nutrients, especially amino acids.

Eating the detox way doesn't have to be expensive. You don't have to buy foods from special stores and you don't have to start eating crazy weird foods. There are a few ingredients that might be new to you or may be only found in health stores, but I give you many options for substitutions so you can keep it simple if you prefer.

And you can definitely make the detox way a lifestyle. If you eat the detox way 90% of the time, your body will thank you millions of times. Your health will improve. And you will experience more energy, better focus, and improved mental and physical strength.

TOP 12 FOODS FOR DETOX

In this section, I'm going to talk about the top 12 foods or food groups that will help your body and your liver with detoxification. As you will see, these foods are heavily incorporated in the recipes in *The Detox Way.*

1. Cruciferous Vegetables

The vegetables in this family are broccoli, cauliflower, cabbage, collard greens, kale, mustard greens, bok choy, and other leafy greens. These foods provide your body with sulfur, a mineral necessary to build certain amino acids needed for the second phase of liver detoxification. They also contain polyphenols, or antioxidants, that reduce the damage of free radicals and fight against some types of cancers.

As I mentioned when talking about vegetables in the *Balance* section, there are advantages to eating these foods both raw and cooked. Enjoy a combination of both. Eat raw broccoli or cauliflower as a snack. Shred some Brussels sprouts, kale and cabbage and make a salad. Check out the *Detox Cauliflower Salad* for a different salad idea. Add these vegetables to frittata, omelet, and stir-fries. Steam, roast, or lightly saute with some garlic, onion, and lemon juice.

When you cook these vegetables, remember that the cooking technique and duration affect the nutrient content. Steaming usually preserves more nutrients than boiling. Roasting enhances the sweetness, texture, and flavor of the vegetables. Avoid boiling with a lot of water, unless you're making a soup or stew and plan to use the cooking water.

2. Aromatic Vegetables

Aromatic vegetables are garlic, onion, shallots, and leaks. These vegetables also have sulfur, needed to build amino acids for phase 2 in liver detoxification pathways. Many of the recipes in *The Detox Way* include garlic and onion.

Shallots resemble onions in flavor but are milder, sweeter, and have less of a bite. They also have a hint of garlic flavor. You can swap shallots for onions in any recipe if you prefer. I don't use onions or shallots in any raw recipes. If you like the flavor of onion in salads but can't tolerate the bite, try shallots instead.

Despite being super detox foods, these vegetables can upset the digestive system. Bacteria in the gut can ferment the fibers in onions, garlic, shallots, and leaks, causing gas, bloating, cramping and possibly diarrhea or constipation. If you have any of these complaints, reduce the amount you use and consider specialized digestive healing meal plan. Visit my website at www. nourzibdeh.com/healthygut for help.

3. Vitamin C Foods

Vitamin C is an antioxidant. It helps activate the enzymes in the first phase of liver detoxification pathways. It also helps your body make glutathione, a very important antioxidant that's even referred to as the master antioxidant.

Vitamin C also helps with the second phase in the liver detoxification. As your liver transitions from phase 1 to phase 2 pathways, intermediate compounds and free radicals that are more damaging than what you started out with will develop. Vitamin C will counter these compounds to protect your tissues from any damage.

Oranges comes to mind first when talking about vitamin C. Other vegetables and fruits, such as bell peppers, broccoli, Brussels sprouts, pineapple, cantaloupe, papaya, and strawberries are excellent sources as well. Vitamin C starts to break down and becomes less potent if exposed to heat, so incorporate these vegetables and fruits raw and fresh as much as possible.

4. Vitamin E Foods

Vitamin E is another antioxidant that will protect from the damage of free radicals and intermediate compounds. Antioxidants work in harmony and you need all of them for maximum protection. For example, vitamin C is soluble in water and protects parts of your tissues and cells that are water-based. Vitamin E is soluble in fats, so it will protect the parts made of fats. A membrane made of fatty acids surrounds every cell in your body, so it's vitamin E that will protect this membrane from free radical damage.

Foods with high vitamin E content are delicious and easy to incorporate. Just to name a few, sunflower seeds, almonds, avocado, spinach, and collard greens contain vitamin E. They are used often in the recipes in *The Detox Way*.

5. Citrus Fruit

The benefit of citrus fruit goes beyond vitamin C. A compound called limonene helps activate the enzymes needed for phase 1 in liver detoxification. The zest or the rind of

citrus fruit contains more limonene than the pulp. Scrub lemons, limes, and oranges thoroughly under water. Grate the skin and add the zest to marinades for chicken or fish, salad dressings, and even smoothies.

6. Protein Foods

Protein provides your body with amino acids needed for the enzymes of phase 2 of liver detoxification. Without these amino acids, the liver gets stuck in phase 1. This is harmful because damaging intermediate compounds have already developed, and the liver is not able to neutralize them so they can be excreted out of the body. The liver will eventually shut down phase 1 and all of the detoxification process if amino acids aren't available to carry through with phase 2 pathways.

There are many clean sources of protein. Eggs are great because they also contain sulfur, the same mineral found in cruciferous and aromatic vegetables needed to build phase 2 amino acids. *The Proteins* section and the *Healthy Protein List* in the cheat sheets sections have more information on the best types of proteins to choose from.

7. Turmeric

Turmeric is a root plant with a strong deep yellow color. Curcumin, the active ingredient in turmeric, activates phase 2 detoxification enzymes. It also prevents the activation of carcinogens, and if there are any carcinogens that are already active, it helps excrete them out of the body.

You can find turmeric root in the produce section and turmeric powder in the spice section of your grocery store. Turmeric powder is used in many vegetable and protein recipes in *The Detox Way*. Add to scrambled eggs, rub on chicken, or season vegetables before roasting. I especially like it on white vegetables like cauliflower and mushroom for a pretty orange color.

You can also incorporate turmeric in drinks. Stir a teaspoon of the powder in warmed coconut or almond milk for a nice soothing drink. Shred the root with some ginger root and add to warm water to make a relaxing detox tea.

Black pepper contains a compound called peperine that boosts the bioavailability of curcumin. When consumed with black pepper, the level of curcumin in the blood is 2000% higher than curcumin alone.[15] Always add a dash of black pepper when you use turmeric; 1/20 teaspoon of black pepper is enough. You can also combine half a teaspoon of black pepper with quarter cup ground turmeric in a spice jar for a quick shortcut.

Always add some oil when cooking because fats boost the absorption of curcumin, along with other antioxidants. Coconut oil and turmeric is a great combination because the medium chain fatty acids (MCTs) in coconut oil are absorbed faster and easier than other fats. That will allow curcumin to be absorbed along the way and bypass the digestive system.

8. Green Tea

Green tea is rich in antioxidants called catechins. Green tea activates phase 2 enzymes in liver detoxification. It neutralizes free radicals and protects cholesterol from oxidization, which is extremely damaging to your heart and puts you at risk of heart attacks. Green tea lowers the risk of diabetes. It even helps with weight loss because it boosts metabolic rate, fat burning, and total energy expenditure.

Catechins in green tea also protect against cancers like breast, prostate, stomach, colon and others. They help your body convert chemical carcinogens to inactive compounds that are easily excreted.

There isn't one recommendation regarding the number of cups of green tea to drink every day. Leading researchers recommend 2 to 3 cups a day. Some studies showed that 4 to 5 cups protect against stomach cancer, and other studies found that 7 cups of green tea a day help with weight loss.

Make it a habit to drink at least one cup of green tea a day and try to incorporate a second cup when possible. In the morning, a warm cup of green tea sets the tone for a detox clean day. In the afternoon, it provides a gentle caffeine source while being calming at the same time.

Don't exceed 10 cups of green tea a day though. In excess, the tannins in tea can cause constipation. It interferes with the absorption of iron, so drink it away from food. Green tea still contains caffeine, and some varieties contain as much caffeine as coffee. Keep that in mind if you have anxiety or insomnia, and consider limiting green tea to the early morning hours.

9. Bone Broth

Bone broth is concentrated in collagen proteins that provide amino acids needed for phase 2 detoxification pathways. When cooked properly, it contains 3 to 4 times more glycine, one of those amino acids, than meats used in regular cooking. Glycine also improves bones and joint health, digestive health, body composition, and the health of your hair, skin, and nails.

In the *Basic Recipes* section, I include a recipe for making bone broth. It's important that you cook bone broth long enough to extract the collagen proteins. You can sip broth right before meals as an appetizer or as a mid-day calming snack. Use it to make soups and stews and to cook rice or quinoa.

Make a large batch and freeze in glass jars in your freezer so you always have some handy. Store-bought broth and stock may not contain adequate amino acids to provide the same health benefits.

10. High Fiber Foods

Fiber helps the body have regular bowel movements that carry toxins out after they were neutralized by the liver through detoxification.

Vegetables and fruit are the best sources of fiber. These include asparagus, broccoli, Brussels sprouts, cabbage, okra, sweet potatoes, apples, oranges, berries, and many more. Nuts and seeds, like flaxseeds, chia, pistachios, almonds and others provide fiber. And grains like steel-cut oats and buckwheat contain fiber too. I talked about all these foods in the first section of this book.

Eating beans and lentils is an easy way to get fiber from food. However, if you suffer from gas, bloating, or stomach pain after eating beans, stick with gentler fiber sources like vegetables and fruit.

11. Probiotic Foods

Probiotics are live bacteria and microbes that offer your body health benefits. Your body contains millions of healthy bacteria concentrated in your digestive tract.

It's important to have healthy gut flora, which means having more beneficial and less harmful bacteria in your gut. Beneficial bacteria improve the integrity and strength of the lining of your digestive tract. This affects detoxification because this lining acts as a barrier that prevents pathogens and chemicals from entering your body. It's your first-line defense.

Some studies show that specific strains of bacteria degrade pesticides.[16] Probiotics found in kimchi, a traditional Korean fermented cabbage, help detoxify PBA.[17] Other probiotic bacterial strains bind to BPA, limiting the amount that gets absorbed into your bloodstream.[18]

Sauerkraut is fermented cabbage that's been gaining more popularity lately. You can also ferment carrots, radishes, and other vegetables at home using salt and water. If you tolerate dairy, kefir is fermented milk and labneh cheese spread is fermented yogurt. Miso and tempeh are fermented soy that may be ok in small amounts.

If you buy sauerkraut or other fermented vegetables from a store, read the label carefully. Choose a product that doesn't contain vinegar or any other preservative. That's because vinegar or preservatives kill bacteria, defeating the purpose of eating fermented probiotic-rich foods. If you ferment vegetables at home, don't add vinegar, just salt and water.

For therapeutic purposes, I typically recommend probiotic supplements for my patients. If you would like help with customized

supplements, you can contact us through the website at www.nourzibdeh.com.

12. Cilantro and Parsley

Cilantro and parsley are bind to heavy metals like lead, mercury, cadmium, and aluminum so they can be eliminated through bowel movements. These heavy metals are neurotoxins that can cause headache, brain fog, depression, pain, and cramps.

Aim for a quarter of a cup of cilantro or parsley on most days for general health. Add them to salsa and salads. Use them as a garnish and eat it! Add to smoothies. Try to incorporate them as a finishing touch in most of your meals.

GLUTEN AND DAIRY

Do you have to eliminate gluten and dairy? Gluten and dairy are not the ultimate enemy for everyone. You would have to decide if avoiding them has health benefits to you.

Gluten is a protein found in wheat, rye, barley and any foods made with or contaminated with them. Celiac disease is an auto-immune disease where the immune cells attack the lining of the digestive tract. There's no cure to celiac disease and someone who has it needs a complete and strict elimination of gluten.

But there are people with negative celiac disease tests who complain of diarrhea and other digestive problems, brain fog, fatigue, and muscle pain when they consume gluten. People in this group have gluten sensitivity, or gluten intolerance, or non-celiac gluten sensitivity. These terms are often used interchangeably. In these individuals, celiac tests come back negative, but eliminating gluten helps them get rid of the symptoms.

A common denominator between people with celiac disease and people who report not tolerating gluten is the high blood level of a protein called zonulin.[19] The cells lining your digestive tract are attached to one another through tight junctions. Zonulin is an inflammatory protein that regulates the permeability of these tight junctions.[20] Increased zonulin concentration indicates inflammation and intestinal permeability, commonly referred to as leaky gut.

With leaky gut, pathogens and their toxins, chemicals from food, and other toxic compounds that pass through the digestive tract can enter the bloodstream. In some people, the combination of genetics, environment, medication use, lack of digestive capacity, nutrient-lacking diet, gut dysbiosis, leaky gut, and potentially other factors we're still discovering trigger autoimmune conditions and food sensitivities. And symptoms of food sensitivities are very similar of symptoms of backed-up detoxification.

For these reasons, if you suffer from fatigue, headache, brain fog, depression, muscle and joint pain, or digestive issues, consider complete removal of gluten from your diet for 30 days. The recipes in *The Detox Way* are all gluten-free.

Even if you don't have a reason to question gluten, you might be eating too much pasta, pizza, burritos, quesadillas, crackers, breads, muffins, pastries, etc. We can agree that these foods are heavy in calories and lack nutrition. Wheat products are so abundant in the typical American diet and replace nutrient-dense foods like vegetables, fruit, beans, herbs, spices, nuts, and seeds. With *The Detox Way*, I encourage you to load up on super foods and give up wheat for a little bit and see how you feel.

Dairy is another common problem food. Many people have sensitivity reactions to dairy proteins found in all types of dairy including milk, soft and hard cheeses, yogurt, butter, ice-cream, etc. Common symptoms of dairy sensitivity include congestion, postnasal drip, sinus pain, acne, eczema, constipation, and other digestive discomforts.

Another component of dairy that can be problematic is lactose. Lactose is a natural sugar found in milk, yogurt, ice cream and soft cheeses. It's not found in hard cheeses or butter. People with lactose intolerance don't have enough of the enzyme lactase to digest lactose. As a result, lactose is fermented by gut bacteria, resulting in gas, bloating, and other digestive problems. People with lactose intolerance might be able to eat a slice of cheddar cheese but not a cup of yogurt.

The best way to know whether dairy is affecting your health negatively or not is to avoid it for 30 days and see how you feel. I often combine a dairy-free and gluten-free diet for my patients. Then I have them introduce dairy for 1–2 weeks and see how they feel. I have them experiment with gluten in a similar way if they don't have celiac disease.

People with autoimmune conditions need to be extra careful with dairy and wheat. Autoimmune conditions include Hashimoto's, celiac disease, Crohn's disease, and rheumatoid arthritis. Gluten proteins resemble certain tissue proteins in the human body. When immune cells see gluten you've eaten through food, they attack it as well as your own tissue, making the autoimmune condition worse. If you have Hashimoto's, gluten triggers your immune cells to attack your thyroid gland even more. Casein, a protein in dairy, is cross-reactive with gluten. This means it resembles the shape of gluten, and people who react to gluten are likely going to react to casein. For help with autoimmune conditions, visit my website at www.nourzibdeh.com/autoimmune.

If you don't have an autoimmune condition or have no symptoms of dairy sensitivity, you can enjoy a small amount of high quality dairy. Stick to 1–2 servings a day. Good quality dairy are those that are fermented because they offer the added benefit of live cultures.

Probiotic dairy products include aged cheeses, plain Greek yogurt, labneh spreadable cheese, and unsweetened kefir. You can add a tablespoon of grated Parmesan to salads, combine ½ cup Greek yogurt with fresh blueberries and cinnamon for a snack, or add kefir to your smoothie. You may also cook with some grass-fed butter every now and then. I talk about grass-fed butter in the *Fats* section.

If you don't have an autoimmune condition and seem to tolerate gluten, choose healthier options and consume them sporadically. The level of inflammatory zonulin protein is elevated after eating gluten in everyone. However, some people feel it more than others. And in some people the effect isn't as pronounced and doesn't last as long.

If you're going to eat bread, opt for either sourdough or sprouted bread. Sourdough bread is made with lactic and acetic acid fermentation, so it contains probiotics that will support your digest tract health. Make sure it's fermented traditionally with sourdough starter and not with additives or processing aids.

Sprouted breads are made from grains that were soaked and allowed to sprout. They are easier to digest and have more of their nutrients available for absorption. They are usually associated with fewer digestive complaints.

If you follow a strict gluten and dairy-free diet and find no improvement in your symptoms, that doesn't necessarily mean they aren't a problem. Something else, in addition to wheat or dairy, can be causing your symptoms. Testing for food sensitivities helps uncover hidden sources of inflammation. If this is your case, visit my website at http://www.nourzibdeh.com/food-sensitivities-testing for more information."

References

[1]Dewanto, V. et al. (2002). Thermal Processing Enhances the Nutritional Value of Tomatoes by Increasing Total Antioxidant Activity. *Journal of Agricultural and Food Chemistry*, 50(10), 3010-3014. .

[2]Talcott, S. T. et al. (2000). Antioxidant Changes and Sensory Properties of Carrot Puree Processed with and without Periderm Tissue. *Journal of Agricultural and Food Chemistry*, 48(4), 1315-1321.

[3] Katz, D. L. et al. (2005). Egg consumption and endothelial function: A randomized controlled crossover trial. *International Journal of Cardiology, 99(1), 65-70.*

[4] Katz, D. L., et al. (2015). Effects of egg ingestion on endothelial function in adults with coronary artery disease: A randomized, controlled, crossover trial. *American Heart Journal*, 169(1), 162-169.

[5] Njike, V. et al. (2010). Daily egg consumption in hyperlipidemic adults - Effects on endothelial function and cardiovascular risk. *Nutrition Journal*, 9(28), 1-9.

[6] Aris, A. et al. (2011). Maternal and fetal exposure to pesticides associated to genetically modified foods in Eastern Townships of Quebec, Canada. *Reproductive Toxicology*, 31(4), 528-533.

[7]Mezzomo, B. P. (2013). Hematotoxicity of Bacillus thuringiensis as Spore-crystal Strains Cry1Aa, Cry1Ab, Cry1Ac or Cry2Aa in Swiss Albino Mice. *Journal of Hematology & Thromboembolic Diseases*, 01(01).

[8] Souza, R. J. et al. (2015). Intake of saturated and trans unsaturated fatty acids and risk of all cause mortality, cardiovascular disease, and type 2 diabetes: *Systematic review and meta-analysis of observational studies*. Bmj.

[9] Siri-Tarino, P. W. et al. (2010). Meta-analysis of prospective cohort studies evaluating the association of saturated fat with cardiovascular disease. *American Journal of Clinical Nutrition*, 91(3), 535-546.

[10] Fats and Fatty Acids in Human Nutrition. (2009). *Annals of Nutrition and Metabolism*; 55 (1–3).

[11]Sachdeva, A. et al. (2009). Lipid levels in patients hospitalized with coronary artery disease: An analysis of 136,905 hospitalizations in Get With The Guidelines. *American Heart Journal*, 157(1).

[12] Daley, C. A. et al. (2010). A review of fatty acid profiles and antioxidant content in grass-fed and grain-fed beef. *Nutrition Journal*, 9(1).

[13] Dhiman, T. et al. (1999). Conjugated Linoleic Acid Content of Milk from Cows Fed Different Diets. *Journal of Dairy Science*, 82(10), 2146-2156.

[14] Whigham, L. D., et al. (2007) Efficacy of Conjugated Linoleic Acid for Reducing Fat Mass: A Meta-Analysis in Humans. *The American Journal of Clinical Nutrition*, 85(5),1203–1211.

[15] Shoba, G. et al. (1998). Influence of Piperine on the Pharmacokinetics of Curcumin in Animals and Human Volunteers. *Planta Medica*, 64(04), 353-356.

[16] Harishankar, M. K. et al. (2012). Efficiency of the intestinal bacteria in the degradation of the toxic pesticide, chlorpyrifos. *3 Biotech*, 3(2), 137-142.

[17] Yamanaka, H. et al (2007). Degradation of bisphenol A by Bacillus pumilus isolated from kimchi, a traditionally fermented food. *Applied Biochemistry and Biotechnology*, 136(1), 39-51.

[18] Oishi, K. et al. Effect of Probiotics, Bifidobacterium breve and Lactobacillus casei, on Bisphenol A Exposure in Rats. Bioscience, Biotechnology, and Biochemistry, 72(6), 1409-1415.

[19] Barbaro MR, et al. (2015). The role of zonulin in non-celiac gluten sensitivity and irritable bowel syndrome. Abstract presented at the 23rd *United European Gastroenterology Week (UEG Week 2015)*. Barcelona, Spain.

[20] Fasano A. (2012) Zonulin, regulation of tight junctions, and autoimmune diseases. *Ann NY Acad Sci.* 1258:25–33.

Cook

RECOMMENDED TOOLS

I try to use basic tools to not clutter my kitchen. This list has the tools you will see used in the recipes. If there's something you don't have, you can always find a replacement or a different tool that will do the job. For example, the small hand juicer I like is small, inexpensive, and efficient. It helps me extract juice from fresh lemons so fast without having to worry about the seeds, and cleaning it is a breeze. You can still get fresh lemon juice without it, but it might be an extra step to separate the seeds or you may not get all the juice from the lemons. If you have a preferred way or tool, you can always stick with that. The list here is just a suggestion based on my experience cooking for my family and myself for over 10 years.

- Large chef knife
- Paring knife
- Cutting board for produce (wood or plastic)
- Dishwasher-safe cutting board for raw meat, fish, poultry
- Y-shaped vegetable peeler
- Kitchen shears (great for snapping herbs and cutting ends of green beans)
- Whisk
- Mortar and pestle (for crushing garlic and ginger to release flavor and juices)
- Grater (shred ginger, lemon and orange zest, etc.)
- Dry measuring cups and spoons
- Liquid measuring cup (1-cup, 1-quart)

- Fine colander (fine enough to hold quinoa)
- Mason jars (or re-used clean glass jars for storing stock)
- Wooden skewers
- Salad spinner
- Stainless steel pots/saucepans (small and medium)
- Stainless steel stock pot (large)
- Cast-iron skillet (6" or 8") –can replace a frying pan
- Medium-size frying pan
- Roasting pan
- Baking pan (9 x 13 inches)
- Cookie sheets for roasting vegetables, 2 count
- Digital food thermometer
- Wooden spoons
- Heat-resistant rubber spatula
- Heat-resistant slotted spoon
- Heat-resistant tongs
- A good quality blender like Vitamix or Blendtech. Other good and less expensive options include Ninja blended, Nutribullet, and Magic bullet,
- Hand blender with metal head (optional)
- Food processor
- Slow cooker. Buy one with a timer. Helps cook meals when you're at work
- Pressure cooker. Helps cook foods when you're pinched for time
- Spiralizer, can be replaced with a shredder if you prefer to not buy another tool

MEASUREMENT CONVERSTIONS

- 1 tablespoon = 3 teaspoons
- 1 cup = 16 tablespoons
- ¼ cup = 4 tablespoons
- 1 pound (lb) = 16 ounces (oz)
- 1 ounce (oz) = 28 grams
- 1 cup fluid = 8 fluid ounces
- 1 cup fluid = 240 ml
- 1 pint = 2 cups

HEALTHY PANTRY, FRIDGE, FREEZER LIST

Oils, Vinegars and Condiments

- Oils for dressings: extra virgin olive and cold-pressed avocado
- Oils for cooking: extra virgin olive oil (if low-medium temperature), avocado oil, grass-fed butter (if using dairy), extra virgin cold-pressed coconut oil, toasted sesame oil (for Asian cooking)
- Vinegars: raw apple cider, balsamic vinegar
- Dijon mustard
- Reduced-sodium soy sauce, tamari sauce (gluten-free soy sauce), or coconut aminos (alternative for people who are soy-sensitive)
- Salsa. Store in the fridge
- Pesto (if using dairy)
- Hot sauces

Seasonings

- Salt: iodized sea salt, pink Himalayan salt
- Dried ground spices: black pepper, cinnamon, allspice, garlic, onion, cumin, cayenne pepper, ginger, nutmeg, turmeric, paprika, fennel, chili powder, curry powder
- Dried herbs: rosemary, thyme, oregano, mint, parsley, basil, celery flakes, bay leaves
- Other: crushed red pepper flakes
- Vanilla extract

Canned/Jarred/Dry

- Tomatoes: a variety of diced, crushed, paste, and sun-dried
- Olives, black or green
- Artichoke hearts or roasted red peppers in water
- Capers
- Salmon in bones, sardine, tuna
- Beans: black, cannelini, kidney beans, garbanzo. Dry is better than canned, but if buying canned, look for a BPA-free can.
- Dry lentils, any color

Grains

- Oats (old fashioned and steel-cut)
- Quinoa
- Buckwheat (flour, hot cereal, Kasha)
- Brown rice, brown Basmati rice, wild rice

Sweeteners (in small amounts)

- Raw local honey
- 100% pure maple syrup
- Coconut or date sugar
- Table sugar (occasional use)
- Stevia

Baking

- A variety of gluten-free flours: almond flour, coconut flour, rice flour, oat flour, and amaranth flours are my favorites. Other options include garbanzo bean flour, quinoa flour, or buckwheat flour. Rotate and experiment to find your favorite.
- Baking powder, baking soda (I prefer baking soda and try to replace when possible)
- Cocoa powder
- Dark chocolate (70–80% cocoa)
- Unsweetened chocolate baking squares

Nuts, Seeds, and Fruits

- Raw walnuts, pecans, almonds, pine nuts, pistachios, cashews. Store in the freezer long term. You don't need all of them all time. Rotate.
- Natural almond butter—no salt, sugar, or hydrogenated oils. Store in fridge.
- Ground flaxseed, chia seeds, hempseeds, sesame, and sunflower seeds. Store in the fridge. You don't need all of them all the time. Rotate.
- Unsweetened coconut flakes stored in fridge, coconut milk in a BPA-free can

- Applesauce—no sugar added
- Dried apricots, prunes, cranberries, raisins, dates, unsweetened banana chips

In the Freezer

- Unsweetened fruit (berries, mangoes, pineapple, peaches)
- Vegetables without sauce (broccoli, cauliflower, chopped spinach, Brussels sprouts, artichoke hearts, peas and carrots, green beans stir-fry mix)
- Meat, poultry, and fish such as salmon or other white fish fillet, peeled shrimp, skinless boneless chicken breasts (whole or cubed), 95% ground beef or turkey, lean stew beef or lamb, lean beef strips
- Salmon or turkey burgers
- Cooked brown rice, quinoa, beans
- Homemade chicken or beef bone broth, stored in glass jars
- Dinner leftovers: either in individual servings or enough for the whole family for dinner
- Pre-cut and marinated chicken or beef. Prepare in advance and use for last minute meals.

Middle Eastern Staples
(extra if you like to!)

- Tahini sauce
- Zaatar (sesame, thyme, and other spices mix)
- Sumac (red spice, has a sour taste)
- Crushed mint leaves
- Pomegranate molasses
- Orange blossom water

Basic Recipes

CHICKEN STOCK WITH CHICKEN MEAT

Homemade chicken stock is more flavorful, cleaner and cheaper than commercial products. This recipe will yield both chicken stock and chicken meat. Use a whole chicken because it will cost you less than buying pieces separately. If a whole chicken is too intimidating, use about 1 pound of chicken breasts and 1 pound of chicken thighs or drumsticks with bones

- 1 whole chicken (or chicken breasts, thighs, and drumsticks)
- 6 garlic cloves, peeled
- 1 medium onion, peeled and quartered
- 4 medium carrots, quartered
- 2 celery stalks, quartered
- 10 generous sprigs fresh thyme
- 10 generous sprigs flat-leaf parsley
- 1 teaspoon peppercorns (or black pepper)
- 1 teaspoon sea salt
- 2 bay leaves
- 4–6 quarts water

Combine all ingredients in a large stockpot. Pour in enough water to cover the chicken completely. Bring water to a boil over medium-high heat. Skim any fat and foam from the surface with a ladle, or large spoon. Reduce the heat and simmer or one hour or until the chicken is completely cooked.

Remove the chicken from the pot and place on a large plate. Let it cool for 10 minutes. Cut the chicken meat from the bones, and reserve for chicken salad, soup, or other recipes. Store in the fridge for up to 5 days and in the freezer for up to 3 months.

Return the bones to the pot and cook for one more hour.

Place a large strainer inside a large bowl or another stockpot. Pour the content of the pot, including the bones, vegetables, and herbs inside the strainer. Lift the strainer up and the broth should be in the bowl. Toss whatever is in the strainer. Now you have stock you can use in many recipes.

Allow the stock to cool at room temperature for no more than 1 hour. Transfer to glass jars, cover, and store in the fridge for up to 4 days or in the freezer for up to 3 months. Remove the layer of fat that developed on the surface for a low-fat option.

Note
Here are tips for freezing. Don't fill the jars all the way to the top because water expands when it freezes. Leave about 1 inch empty in the top. You can also freeze in an ice-cube tray then transfer to a plastic bag once the cubes are completely frozen. Label the jars or bags with the content and the date. Store extra shredded chicken in glass containers or freezer bags labeled.

CHICKEN STOCK (WITHOUT CHICKEN MEAT)

Homemade chicken stock is more flavorful and cheaper than commercial varieties. It has healing elements that boost your immune system, digestion, and gut integrity. Your grandmother knew what she was doing when she made chicken soup!

This recipe will yield just chicken stock. You can use necks, backs, wings, or bones leftover from rotisserie chicken or roasted chicken.

2 pounds chicken bones, including necks, backs, wings
2 garlic cloves, peeled
1 medium onion, peeled and quartered
2 medium carrots, quartered
2 celery stalks, quartered
4 generous sprigs fresh thyme
4 generous sprigs flat-leaf parsley
½ teaspoon black pepper
1 teaspoon sea salt
2 bay leaves
2–4 quarts water

Combine all ingredients in a large stockpot. Bring water to a boil over medium-high heat. Skim any fat and foam from the surface with a ladle, or large spoon. Reduce the heat and simmer for two hours. Check regularly to remove any scum that develops and ensure there's enough water.

Place a large strainer inside a large bowl. Pour the content of the pot, including the bones, vegetables, and herbs inside the strainer. Lift the strainer up and the broth should be in the bowl. Toss whatever is in the strainer. Now you have stock you can use in many recipes.

Allow the stock to cool at room temperature for no more than 1 hour. Transfer to glass jars, cover, and store in the fridge for up to 4 days or in the freezer for up to 3 months. Remove the layer of fat that developed on the surface for a low-fat option

Note

Here are tips for freezing. Don't fill the jars all the way to the top because water expands when it freezes. Leave about 1 inch empty in the top.

You can also freeze in an ice-cube tray then transfer to a plastic bag once the cubes are completely frozen.

Label the jars or bags with the content and the date.

Store extra shredded chicken in glass containers or freezer bags labeled.

SHREDDED CHICKEN BREAST

Makes 4 4-ounce servings

....

1 – 1.5 pounds chicken breasts

½ teaspoon sea salt

¼ teaspoon black pepper

¼ teaspoon garlic powder

½ teaspoon oregano

2 tablespoons olive oil

Juice of half a lemon

Directions in Slow Cooker

Place chicken breasts in a slow cooker.

Sprinkle the salt, black pepper, garlic, oregano, olive oil, and lemon juice. Rub to distribute evenly.

Add 4 cups of water. Cover and cook on low for 4 hours.

Remove the chicken from the saucepan and shred. Use immediately or store in the fridge for 4 days. You can also place in freezer bags and store for 3 months.

Directions on the Stove

Heat the olive oil in a medium size saucepan.

Add chicken breast and sear it on each side for 1–2 minutes. Season it with salt, black pepper, garlic powder, oregano, and lemon juice.

Add water and bring to a boil. Simmer on low heat for 30–60 minutes or until chicken is completely cooked.

Remove the chicken from the saucepan and shred. Use immediately or store in the fridge for 4 days. You can also place in freezer bags and store for 3 months.

Note

You can also make this recipe with just the salt and pepper. This way, you can use the chicken in several dishes and add specific spices and herbs when needed.

BONE BROTH

4 pounds beef bones from grass-fed cows (or organic if you can't find grass-fed). A combination of beef soup bones or beef marrow bones recommended

2 tablespoons raw apple cider vinegar or juice of 1 lemon

3 carrots, quartered

3 celery stalks, quartered

1 onion

½ head garlic, peeled

10 generous sprigs of fresh parsley

2 teaspoons salt (or more to taste)

2 teaspoons black pepper (or more to taste)

Place beef bones in a slow cooker. Sprinkle with apple cider vinegar or lemon juice. Cover with water and cook on low heat for 12 hours or overnight. Skim any fat or foam from the top using a large spoon.

Add carrots, celery, onion, garlic, parsley, salt, and pepper. Cook for another 12 hours.

Strain into a large bowl or another pot using a mesh strainer.

Fill the sink or a large box with ice and immerse the bowl with the stock to cool. Place in the fridge overnight. The following day, remove the layer of fat on the surface.

Pour into glass jars (12, 16, or 18-ounce jars depending on how you plan to use the broth). Store some in the refrigerator for up to 4 days. Store the remaining in the freezer for up to 3 months.

Note

To extract the nutrients from the bones, longer cooking time is required.

The broth can be used in cooking or soups. Also consider drinking it in a coffee cup any time in the day as a hot drink.

Freeze extra broth in labeled glass jars. Include the date.

HARD-BOILED EGGS

Serves 1

2 large eggs

Place enough water to cover the eggs in a small size saucepan. Bring to a boil.

Add the eggs, one at a time, using a spoon to prevent the eggs from breaking.

Lower the heat and simmer for 8–10 minutes. Less time if you prefer the yolks to be runny.

Remove the eggs from the pot and soak in cold water for few more minutes to immediately stop the eggs from cooking further.

Peel when ready to eat.

Note

Having few boiled eggs in your fridge helps with meal planning. Boil 6–8 at a time. Peel and then store in the fridge. Grab one for a light breakfast or snack on the go, or grab two to add to salads for lunch.

BASIC SALAD DRESSING

Makes 5-6 servings

1 medium garlic clove, crushed

¼ cup extra virgin olive oil

2 tablespoons raw apple cider or balsamic

vinegar

Juice of 1 lemon, about 4 tablespoons

¼ teaspoon ground mustard

¼ teaspoon salt

¼ teaspoon ground black pepper

½ teaspoon dried oregano or crushed thyme leaves

Combine all ingredients in a small bowl or glass jar and whisk.

Use immediately.

Store leftover in the fridge for up to 2 weeks. When ready to use, let it sit in room temperature for 15–20 minutes. Shake well before tossing with salad ingredient.

Note

You may use different oils (like avocado oil or almond oil), vinegars (like rice vinegar), or herbs (like basil, rosemary, parsley, sage, etc.) to change up the recipe. You may add more vinegar if you like a stronger flavor.

Olive oil naturally solidifies at refrigeration temperature. Unlike commercial dressings, this dressing will solidify in the fridge because it doesn't have chemical agents that keep olive oil liquid in the fridge temperature. Plus, most commercial dressings are not made with 100% olive oil to begin with. Take the dressing out of the fridge 15–20 minutes before serving.

STEAMED VEGETABLES

Serves 4

....

1 pound of fresh vegetables like broccoli, carrots, green beans, cauliflower, cabbage, etc.

1 tablespoon extra virgin olive oil

Sea salt to taste

Ground black pepper to taste

Freshly squeezed lemon juice to taste

Cut your vegetables into uniform sizes so they cook at the same speed.

Add an inch or two of water to the saucepan then insert the steaming basket. The water should be under the basket and not touch the vegetables.

Bring the water to boil. Add the vegetables, cover, and lower the heat to medium. Set the timer.

Steam. The cooking time depends on the vegetable. Spinach, arugula, and green peas take about 3 minutes. Broccoli, cauliflower, green beans, kale, and collard greens take about 5–7 minutes. Carrots, potatoes, turnips, and squash take 10–20 minutes.

Remove the vegetables when tender. A knife should easily be able to pierce the vegetables. Don't leave them to steam for too long to keep their crunchiness.

To serve, drizzle with some olive oil, sea salt, black pepper, garlic powder, and freshly squeezed lemon juice.

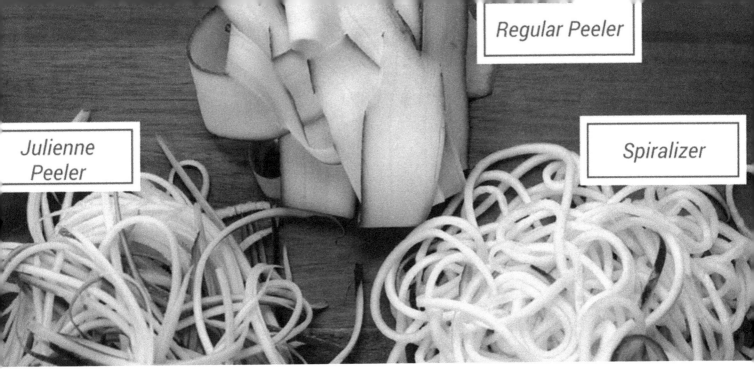

Julienne Peeler

Regular Peeler

Spiralizer

ZUCCHINI NOODLES

Serves 4

½ tablespoon extra virgin olive oil

4 medium zucchinis

2 garlic cloves, chopped

1 teaspoon dried basil or oregano

Sea salt and black pepper to taste

Freshly squeezed lemon juice to taste

Wash each zucchini and cut off the ends. Peel any bruised parts of the skin if needed.

Spiralizer: use the blade with the smallest holes to create spaghetti-like noodles. Attach the center of the zucchini to the little circle in the center of the blade then press the handle so that the pins attach to the zucchini. Turn the handle while pushing the zucchini towards the blade. Collect the noodles from the other side. You may cut them in half since they will be very long. Use the core for stews, soups, or frittata.

Regular or julienne peeler: grip the zucchini with one hand and peel from one side. When you reach the seeds, turn and peel from the remaining sides. Use the core for stews, soups, or frittata.

Heat the olive oil in a medium saucepan on medium heat. Saute the garlic for 1 minute. Add the zucchini, dried herbs, salt and pepper. Saute for 5 minutes or more depending on your preference for texture.

Note

Keep the zucchini skin for more fiber. Try yellow squash noodles. Carrots, beets, butternut squash, potatoes, and sweet potatoes are fun to spiral as well, but remember that they are heavier in carbs than zucchini. Use these noodles with The Veggie Lovers Spaghetti in the 3-in-1 Meals section

DRY BEANS ON THE STOVETOP

One pound of dry beans makes about five cups of cooked beans, about 3 cans of canned beans.

....

1 pound dried beans, like white beans, black beans, garbanzo beans

(see note about kidney beans)

Water

2 to 3 teaspoons salt, plus more to taste

Put beans in a large bowl and sort through. Remove any stones or twigs, or any shriveled beans. Soak in water overnight.

Drain the soaked beans with a colander. Place in a large pot and cover with fresh water.

Bring the water to a boil. Cover the pot with a lid and simmer gently on medium heat for 1–2 hours. Check the beans for doneness after the first hour. Add more water if needed to make sure they are completely covered. Season with salt when they are almost finished cooking.

When cooked, turn the heat off and let the beans cool in their cooking liquid. Transfer to containers or glass jars, along with the liquid. Store in the fridge for 5 days or the freezer for up to 3 months.

Note

Red kidney beans need to be boiled for 10 minutes to neutralize a toxic compound called phytohemagglutinin that can cause digestive discomforts.

You can add herbs and spices to the beans like celery, carrots, parsley, cumin, coriander, pepper, etc. However, you may decide to add those half way through the cooking process so that they don't get too soft.

DRY BEANS IN THE SLOW COOKER

One pound of dry beans makes about five cups of cooked beans, about 3 cans of canned beans.

....

1 pound dried beans, like white beans, black beans, garbanzo beans

(see note about kidney beans)

Water

2 to 3 teaspoons salt, plus more to taste

Put beans in a large bowl and sort through. Remove any stones or twigs, or any shriveled beans. Soak with water overnight.

Drain the soaked beans with a colander. Place in the slow cooker. Pour enough water to cover by 2 inches. Cover the slow cooker tightly and let the beans cook on low heat for 5–8 hours. After 5 hours, check for doneness to make sure they don't get too soft. Continue to cook for longer as needed. Season with salt when they are almost finished cooking.

When cooked, turn the heat off and let the beans cool in their cooking liquid. Transfer to containers or glass jars, along with the liquid. Store in the fridge for 5 days or the freezer for up to 3 months.

Note

Red kidney beans need to be boiled for 10 minutes to neutralize a toxic compound called phytohemagglutinin that can cause digestive discomforts. Boil them for 10 minutes first then add to the slow cooker.

You can add herbs and spices to the beans like celery, carrots, parsley, cumin, coriander, pepper, etc. However, you may decide to add those half way through the cooking process so that they don't get too soft.

EVERYDAY LENTILS

Makes 4-5 cups cooked lentils, about 4-5 servings

2 cups uncooked lentils, brown, orange, yellow or other color (some colors may cook faster than others)

½ **teaspoon sea salt**

1 **teaspoon extra virgin** olive oil

Seasonings and herbs as desired

Spread lentils over a flat surface like plate or cutting board. Remove any rocks or dirt. Place in a strainer and rinse with water.

Transfer the lentils to a medium size pot. Add double the amount of water because lentils will absorb a lot of water as they cook.

Bring the water to a boil. Then reduce the heat, cover, and let them simmer for 20 to 30 minutes. Check on the water and add more if there isn't enough to cover the lentils.

The lentils are cooked when soft and no longer raw or crunchy. Season with olive oil and sea salt. You can also season with cumin, garlic, and black pepper. Sprinkle some fresh or dried oregano, thyme, basil, and/or lemon juice.

Eat lentils as a snack, add to salads, or eat them as part of a dinner meal. Count them in the Carbohydrate portion of your plate.

EVERYDAY QUINOA

Serves 4

....

1 cup uncooked quinoa

2 cups water or chicken or bone broth

¼ teaspoon sea salt

Herbs and seasoning as desired like basil,

oregano, cilantro, parsley, garlic, ginger

Place quinoa in a fine mesh strainer. Rinse thoroughly with water to remove the natural compounds that give quinoa a bit of a bitter taste.

Combine quinoa, water, and sea salt in a medium pan. Bring to a boil. Reduce the heat and simmer covered until the liquid is absorbed, about 15–20 minutes. Flake with a fork.

Add desired herbs and seasonings.

EVERYDAY RICE

Serves 4

....

**1 cup of brown long grain
or basmati rice**

½ tablespoon extra virgin

olive oil

¼ teaspoon sea salt

Herbs and seasoning

**as desired like basil,
oregano, cilantro,
parsley, garlic, ginger**

Place rice in a fine mesh strainer. Rinse
thoroughly with water.

Bring 2 cups of water to a boil in a medium
pot. Stir in the rice, salt, and olive oil. Bring
to a gentle simmer. Turn the heat down,
cover, and cook for 20–30 minutes.

Add any herbs or spices if desired.

Note

*This recipe is for making long grain rice that
flakes. There are many other rice variations
that require different cooking techniques*

EVERYDAY BAKED POTATO OR SWEET POTATO

Serves 4

....

4 small or 2 large white, or baking, or sweet   **potatoes**

½ tablespoon avocado oil

Preheat the oven to 375°F.

Wash the potatoes thoroughly with a vegetable brush to remove any dirt or soil. Remove any bruised parts. Pierce each potato 5 to 6 times with a fork or knife.

Place the potatoes whole on a piece of foil paper large enough to wrap around them. Drizzle the olive oil.

Wrap with the foil paper and place on a small baking sheet. Bake in the oven for 45 minutes. They are done when you can insert a knife in the potato and pull it back easily.

Breakfast Recipes

EVERYDAY VEGETABLE OMELET

Serves 1

....

2 teaspoons extra virgin olive oil, divided

4 asparagus spears, about ½ cup chopped

2–3 broccoli florets, about ½ cup chopped

1 small tomato, about ½ cup diced

2 large eggs

A dash of sea salt

A dash of ground black pepper

A dash or garlic powder

Prepare the vegetables first. Wash the asparagus and snap the bottom quarter of each spear using your hands. Chop into ½-inch sticks. Cut the broccoli floret into small pieces. Dice the tomato.

In a frying pan, heat 1 teaspoon of olive oil on medium heat. Add the vegetables and saute for 2 minutes.

Meanwhile, whisk the eggs in a small bowl. Make sure you incorporate as much air as possible.

Add the second teaspoon of olive oil to the pan. Pour the eggs over the vegetables, making sure they are spread evenly in the pan. Cook until the eggs set, about 2–3 minutes.

Transfer to a plate.

Note

Serve with a piece of fruit or ½ cup of beans. You can also serve with 2 tablespoons guacamole or 2 avocado slices on the side. You can use any vegetables to make an omelet. Try spinach, peppers, mushroom, onion, kale, zucchini, or summer squash.

POACHED EGGS

Serves 1

....

1 teaspoon extra virgin olive oil   **2 large eggs**

Bring 1 inch of water to a boil in a medium size pot with lid. Lower heat to simmering.

Brush egg poachers with some olive oil. Place in the pot.

Break the eggs into the poachers. Cover and simmer for 4–6 minutes until cooked to desired consistency.

Serve with guacamole, tomatoes, spinach, roasted vegetables, etc.

Note

While you can certainly poach eggs in water without any tools, I find that it's easier to use egg poachers. Look for one in stores that sell household items. Visit our website at www.nourzibdeh.com/shop for recommendations.

MIXED VEGETABLE FRITTATA

Serves 4

½ tablespoon coconut or avocado oil

2 cups chopped mushroom

1 small zucchini, chopped

1 bell pepper, chopped

8 eggs

¼ cup coconut milk

¼ teaspoon salt

¼ teaspoon pepper

¼ teaspoon garlic

3 scallions (green onion), sliced

Preheat the oven to 400°F.

Heat oil in a cast iron skillet. If you don't have one, use a skillet without plastic handles that can go inside the oven.

Sauté the mushrooms, pepper, and zucchini until soft. Meanwhile, whisk the eggs with the coconut milk in a medium bowl. Season with salt, pepper, and garlic.

Pour the egg mixture over the vegetables., making sure they are distributed evenly. Top with the green onion slices. Continue to cook for about 5 minutes until eggs start to set around the edges.

Transfer the skillet to the oven and cook for 20 minutes.

Note

You may use other vegetables like are broccoli, cauliflower, spinach, kale, bok choy, or shredded carrots and other herbs like parsley, cilantro, basil, or dill. Cast iron skillets get very hot so avoid sautéing with olive oil because it will not tolerate the heat.

This meal doesn't contain any carbohydrates. Enjoy it with a side of fruit or half a cup of beans or baked sweet potato.

EGG AVOCADO SALAD

Serves 1

2 hard-boiled eggs (see basic recipes for instructions if needed)

½ avocado

½ orange, red, or yellow bell pepper

2 tablespoons cilantro

2 tablespoons lemon juice

Sea salt and ground black pepper to taste

Peel the hard-boiled egg. Cut into cubes and place in a bowl.

Cut the avocado in half. Use the side without the pit. Holding the avocado in your least dominant hand with flesh facing up, use a knife to make few horizontal and vertical cuts. Scoop out the avocado flesh with a spoon.

Dice the bell pepper and chop the cilantro.

Add to the eggs and avocado.

Drizzle lemon juice and season with salt and pepper to taste. Fold the ingredients until combined well.

BLACK BEAN EGG BAKE

Serves 6

1 tablespoon avocado oil
plus extra for coating
the baking dish

12 eggs

1½ cups black beans,
(about 1 BPA-free can),
rinsed and drained

2 cups broccoli, cut into
small florets

1 cup cauliflower, cut into
small florets

½ c cilantro, chopped

1 teaspoon sea salt

1 teaspoon ground black
pepper

Coat a 9 x 13 baking dish with avocado oil.
Preheat the oven to 350°F.

In a large bowl, whisk the eggs thoroughly.
Add the tablespoon of oil, beans, broccoli,
cauliflower, cilantro, salt and pepper.

Pour into the baking dish. Cook in the oven
for 30–40 minutes until the eggs are golden
from top and no longer liquid. You can
insert a toothpick to check. Let it cool for
5–10 minutes. Cut into 6 servings.

Note

*To make in advance, let it cool completely
then store in the fridge or freezer. You can
cut into smaller portions and serve as a
snack. Since it's low in carbohydrates, you
may serve this dish with a cup of berries.*

*You can replace the beans with 1.5 cups
cooked and mashed potato or sweet
potato, or with 1.5 cups shredded raw
potato or sweet potato.*

WHOLE CHIA SEED PUDDING

Serves 4

3 cups almond or coconut milk, unsweetened

½ cup chia seeds

1 tablespoon 100% pure maple syrup

½ cup slivered almonds for topping (optional, for topping)

1 cup fresh blueberries and/or cut-up strawberries (for topping)

Whisk together almond or coconut milk, chia seeds, and maple syrup in a large bowl. Refrigerate overnight or 3–4 hours at minimum.

Stir well before serving. Scoop desired amount in your serving bowl. Top with fresh berries and slivered almonds.

NUTTY FRUIT BREAKFAST

Serves 1

....

1 teaspoon coconut oil

1 medium apple or pear, cored and cut into small cubes

2 tablespoons chopped walnuts

2 tablespoons slivered almonds

½ tablespoon chia seeds

½ teaspoon cinnamon

¼ teaspoon nutmeg

½ teaspoon pure maple syrup (optional)

In a small saucepan, heat the coconut oil. Add the apple pieces and cook for 1–2 minutes, until desired texture. Add 1 teaspoon of water if you need more juice. Transfer to a bowl.

Top with walnuts, almonds, chia seeds, cinnamon, nutmeg, and maple syrup. Toss to combine.

Note

You can make this recipe with 1 peach or 1 cup mango, berries, blueberries, etc. You can leave the fruit raw.

To make this for a large group, double, or triple or even quadruple the recipe. Combine the apples and coconut oil in a baking sheet and bake at 350 for 20 minutes. Then add the nuts and seasonings and toss.

EVERYDAY OATMEAL

Serves 1

¼ cup plain old-fashioned rolled oats or steel-cut oats

¼ cup nuts and seeds (slivered almonds, walnuts, chia, hemp, flax, pecan, hazelnut, etc.)

¼ teaspoon cinnamon

½ cup chopped fresh ripe fruit (blueberries, bananas, strawberries, apples, pears, peaches, etc.)

Cook oats in water according to package instructions. If using rolled oats, cook on the stovetop or microwave for 1–2 minutes. If using steel-cut oats, cook on the stovetop.

Add nuts and seeds, cinnamon, and fresh fruit.

Note

Rolled oats and steel-cut oats are very comparable in calorie, carbohydrate, protein, and fiber content. Use whichever type you prefer.

MUESLI

Serves 6

1 cup old-fashioned rolled oats

1 cup nuts like slivered almonds, chopped walnuts, peanuts, hazelnuts, sunflower seeds, pumpkin seeds (pepita), etc.

⅓ cup chia seeds

⅓ cup shredded unsweetened coconut

1 cup dried fruit like chopped prunes, apricots, dates or raisins

2 teaspoon ground

cinnamon

Optional: 1 teaspoon cocoa powder or 2 tablespoons dark chocolate chips

½ cup coconut or almond milk

Combine the oats, nuts, chia seeds, coconut, dried fruit, and any other optional ingredient in an air-tight container.

Store in your pantry for up to 4 weeks.

To serve, combine 1 cup of muesli with 1 cup of coconut or almond milk in a bowl with a lid. Stir, cover, and refrigerate overnight. Eat the following morning—it will be soft and moist.

Alternatively, eat the muesli raw without soaking. Combine a cup of muesli with coconut or almond milk and eat right away.

SWEET POTATO PANCAKES

Serves 6

....

1 cup pureed sweet potato
   (make fresh from 1
   medium sweet potato or
   BPA-free can)

1 cup almond flour

½ cup rice flour

¼ teaspoon baking soda

1 teaspoon cinnamon

2 eggs

½ teaspoon vanilla

2 tablespoons avocado oil

1 tablespoon pure maple
   syrup

1 teaspoon raw apple cider
   vinegar

If you're starting with a fresh sweet potato, wrap it in foil and bake in the oven for 1 hour at 400°F. Cool, peel, and puree using a food processor. You can also mash with a fork if it's soft enough. This step can be done few days in advance.

In a medium bowl, combine the almond flour, rice flour, baking soda, and cinnamon. In another medium bowl, whisk the eggs. Mix in the pureed sweet potato, vanilla, avocado oil, maple syrup, and vinegar.

Add the dry ingredients to the liquid ingredients and mix until combined.

If the batter is dry, add 1–2 tablespoons of water, one at a time. It will be thicker than typical pancake batters.

Lightly coat a griddle or non-stick saute pan with some avocado oil and heat on medium. Ladle about ¼ cup at a time. Shape to make circles.

Cook until the bottom is golden. Flip and cook until the other side is golden.

Enjoy with some fresh fruit. Store leftovers in the fridge for few days.

Note

This recipe is a great way to use leftover sweet potatoes. If you don't have almond flour, place raw almonds in a food processor and process until ground.

Lunches
and
Dinners

Side Soups

BASIC VEGETABLE SOUP

Serves 6

1 tablespoon olive oil

1 small onion, chopped

4 garlic cloves, chopped

2 celery stalks, chopped

2 large carrots, chopped

1 large zucchini, chopped

1 cup kale or spinach, chopped

2 tomatoes on the vine, chopped

½ teaspoon sea salt

¼ teaspoon ground black pepper

½ teaspoon ground allspice

¼ teaspoon cinnamon

¼ teaspoon turmeric

4–6 cups chicken stock, see pages 72 and 73 (water is also ok if you don't have stock)

½ cup parsley, chopped, for garnish

Heat the olive oil in a medium size pan on medium heat. Add the onion and sauté for 1 minute. Add the garlic, celery and carrots, and saute for 1–2 more minutes.

Add the zucchini, kale and tomatoes. Season with sea salt, black pepper, allspice, cinnamon, and turmeric.

Add 4 cups of chicken stock or water and simmer on low heat for 20–30 minutes. Check often and add more water if needed.

Garnish with parsley right before serving.

Note

This recipe is low in carbohydrates and a great way to increase your vegetable and water intake. Eat it at the beginning of your meal and it will help you feel satisfied.

MIDDLE EASTERN PUREED RED LENTIL SOUP

Serves 6

- 1 tablespoon olive oil
- 1 medium onion, cut into quarters
- 4 garlic cloves, whole
- 2 cups red dry lentils, rinsed with water
- 2 large carrots, peeled and cut into large cubes
- 2 tomatoes on the vine, quartered
- ½ teaspoon sea salt
- ½ teaspoon pepper
- ½ teaspoon allspice
- 1 teaspoon ground cumin
- Fresh lemon juice to serve
- Parsley or cilantro as garnish

Heat the oil in a large pot over medium heat. Saute the onion and garlic for 2 minutes. Add lentils, carrots, and tomatoes. Season with salt, pepper, allspice, and cumin.

Add water to cover vegetables plus 2 inches over. Bring to a boil then simmer on medium-low heat for 30 minutes, or until all vegetables are soft. Check regularly as lentils absorb water and may dry out. You may need to add more water.

Using a handheld blender, puree in the pot. Alternatively, transfer to a blender and puree. If you prefer a thinner soup, add more water.

To serve, garnish with parsley or cilantro. Squeeze fresh lemon juice right before eating.

Note

Freeze individual portions of leftover soup in freezer-safe containers like glass jars. Enjoy for many lunches to come.

CHUNKY BROWN LENTIL SOUP

Serves 6

....

1 tablespoon olive oil

½ onion, chopped

2 garlic cloves, chopped

2 celery stalks, chopped

1½ cups dry brown lentils, rinsed with water

1 cup carrots, chopped

(about 3 carrots)

3 small tomatoes, chopped

½ teaspoon sea salt

½ teaspoon ground black pepper

½ teaspoon cumin

½ teaspoon coriander

¼ teaspoon cardamom

4–6 cups chicken stock, see pages 72 and 73 (water is also ok if you don't have stock)

2 bay leaves

Fresh lemon juice to serve

Heat the olive oil in a medium pot over medium heat. Add the onion and garlic and sauté for 2 minutes.

Add the celery, lentils, carrots, and tomatoes. Season the vegetables with salt, pepper, cumin, coriander, and cardamom.

Add the chicken stock and bay leaves. Simmer on medium-low heat for 20 minutes. Add more water if you prefer a thinner soup.

To serve, squeeze fresh lemon juice over the soup.

CURRIED BUTTERNUT SQUASH SOUP

Serves 6

....

1 whole butternut squash, about 5 cups diced

1 medium apple, any type

1 small onion

½ tablespoon coconut oil, melted

2 cups coconut milk

2 cups chicken stock, see pages 72 and 73 (water is also ok if you don't have stock)

2 teaspoons curry powder

½ teaspoon cinnamon

¼ teaspoon turmeric

¼ teaspoon cayenne

For garnish (optional): unsweetened coconut flakes, chopped cashews, red pepper flakes

Peel the butternut squash. Cut in half lengthwise. Clean out the seeds and cut into large cubes. You can eliminate this step if you find cubed butternut squash in your grocery store.

Peel and core the apple. Cut into cubes. Chop the onion into large pieces.

Heat the coconut oil in a medium size pan. Saute the onion for 2 minutes. Add the butternut squash and apple chunks.

Add the coconut milk, chicken stock, curry powder, cinnamon, turmeric, and cayenne. Simmer for 20–30 minutes or until the butternut squash and apple are soft.

Transfer to a blender to puree or use a hand-held blender. Add more water if you prefer a thinner soup.

Serve hot. Garnish with coconut flakes, chopped cashews, or red pepper flakes if desired.

Note

This recipe is low in protein. You can take it to work with 2 hard-boiled eggs or leftover roasted chicken.

If you want to serve it as an appetizer, eliminate other carbohydrate sources from your meal. For example, pair with baked salmon and a salad.

TOMATO CLAM CHOWDER

Serves 2

....

1 tablespoon olive oil

1 onion, chopped

2 garlic cloves, chopped

2 celery stalks, diced

2 carrots, diced

2 tomatoes on the vine or plum, diced

1 bell pepper, diced

2 bay leaves

1 teaspoon thyme or oregano

2 tablespoons tomato paste

½ pound clam meat, thawed, if frozen

1 cup frozen green peas

Sea salt and pepper to taste

In a medium-size pot, heat the olive oil. Sauté the onion and garlic until soft and translucent. Add the celery, carrots, tomatoes, and bell peppers and saute for few minutes. Season with some sea salt and pepper.

Add water, about 2–4 cups, bay leaves, thyme or oregano, and tomato paste. Simmer on low heat for 20 minutes.

Add the clam meat and green peas. Simmer for 10 more minutes. Adjust the salt and pepper if needed. Serve hot.

Side Salads

All these side salads can be made into main dish salads.

Mix in a protein source like grilled or shredded chicken, grilled fish, steak, shrimp, or hard-boiled eggs. Check the Protein Dishes section for ideas.

Mix in a carbohydrate source if the recipe doesn't already contain beans, grains, or fruit. In the note section of each recipe, I tell you if it's ok to add another carbohydrate or not.

Since we're aiming for 2 carbohydrate servings per meal, you can add one of these options to your side salad:
- 1 cup cooked beans or peas
- ⅔ cup cook quinoa
- 1 cup fresh fruit like berries, grapes, or diced apple
- ¼ cup dried fruit like raisins or cranberries (choose unsweetened)

CHOPPED KALE SALAD WITH ALMOND VINAIGRETTE

Serves 4

- **8 Brussels sprouts, about 2 cups shredded**
- **6 cups kale, about 1 bunch**
- **3 tablespoons balsamic vinegar, divided**
- **3 tablespoons lemon juice,** divided
- **1 tablespoon olive oil**
- **1 tablespoon almond butter**
- **¾ teaspoon sea salt**
- **¼ teaspoon black pepper**
- **1 yellow or orange bell pepper** sliced
- **2 cups grape tomatoes, cut in half**
- **½ cup packed parsley, chopped**
- **¼ cup sliced almonds**

Trim the ends of the Brussels spouts off, removing any damaged leaves. Cut each in half then place on a cutting board with the flat side down. Thinly slice. Separate any pieces that are stuck together.

To shred the kale, remove the stems. Stack the leaves on top of each other and cut lengthwise in half then thinly slice.

Combine the kale and Brussels sprouts in a large bowl. Add 1 tablespoon balsamic vinegar, 1 tablespoon lemon juice, and 1 tablespoon olive oil. Rub with your hands, making sure all pieces are covered. Set aside.

Make the dressing. Whisk the almond butter, remaining balsamic vinegar, lemon juice, sea salt, and black pepper.

When ready to serve, add the bell pepper, tomatoes, parsley, and almonds to the Brussels sprouts and kale.

Drizzle the dressing and toss to combine.

Note

If desired, replace Brussels sprouts with white or red cabbage, kale with spinach or arugula, and sliced almonds with walnuts, pecans, pine nuts, pumpkin seeds, or sunflower seeds. Add 1/2 cup berries or diced apples if you like a sweet taste. For convenience, look for shredded Brussels sprouts in your grocery store.

ARUGULA AND FENNEL SALAD WITH ORANGE VINAIGRETTE

Serves 4

- 6 cups arugula (about a 10-ounce bag)
- 2 cups sliced fresh mushroom
- 1 cup thinly sliced fennel bulb, about half a bulb
- 2 tablespoons sunflower seeds
- ¼ cup extra virgin olive oil
- 2 tablespoons balsamic vinegar
- Zest and juice of ½ orange
- ¾ teaspoon sea salt
- ¼ teaspoon black pepper
- 1 teaspoon oregano

In a large bowl, combine the arugula, mushroom, fennel, and sunflower seeds.

To make the dressing, whisk together the olive oil, balsamic vinegar, orange juice and zest, sea salt, black pepper, and oregano. Drizzle over the salad and toss when ready to eat.

Note

Some people feel that arugula has a tangy flavor. Try to vary your greens. If it's not one of your favorites, you can stick with spinach, kale, or lettuce.

Make this a main dish salad by adding a protein and carbohydrate. Fruit, like 1 cup of strawberries in the summer and pomegranate seeds in the winter, will go well with this recipe.

DETOX CAULIFLOWER SALAD

Serves 4

....

½ cauliflower head

4 cups broccoli

1 apple (Fuji, Gala, or other sweet apple variety)

½ cup parsley

1 cup shredded carrots

2 tablespoons sunflower seeds

¼ cup raisins or cranberries, unsweetened

3 tablespoons extra virgin olive oil

2 tablespoons balsamic vinegar

1 tablespoon freshly squeezed lemon juice

½ teaspoon sea salt

¼ teaspoon black pepper

2 teaspoons mustard

1 teaspoon oregano

Break the half cauliflower head into small florets. Wash thoroughly. Chop to about ¼ inch pieces. Wash the broccoli and cut into similar size.

Peel the apple and cut into similar size pieces. Chop the parsley.

In a large bowl, combine the chopped cauliflower, broccoli, apple, parsley, carrots, sunflower seeds, and raisins.

In a glass cup or jar, combine the olive oil, balsamic vinegar, lemon juice, sea salt, black pepper, mustard, and oregano. Shake or mix well.

Drizzle the dressing over the vegetables. Toss to make sure all vegetables are coated well.

Note

This is a very different detox salad! Serve it with a protein like salmon, hard-boiled eggs, or grilled chicken to make a complete meal. No need to add any carbohydrates since it contains an apple and raisins (or cranberries) already. The vegetables won't wilt so this is a great salad to make overnight or in the morning and take to work for lunch.

CHICKPEA MANGO FUSION SALAD

Serves 4

2 cups cooked chickpeas

1 red bell pepper, chopped

1 ripe mango, peeled and chopped

1 cup cilantro leaves, chopped

1 tablespoon extra virgin olive oil

¼ teaspoon sea salt

¼ teaspoon ground black pepper

1 teaspoon cumin

½ lime, juiced (or more, to taste)

Combine all ingredients in a bowl. Chill in the fridge for at least an hour before serving.

Count this salad as your carbohydrate quarter of the plate. It goes best with fish like flounder, mahi mahi, or salmon.

Note

To cook chickpeas from scratch, check pages 80 and 81. If you prefer canned chickpeas, pick a BPA-free can or BPA-free carton.

AVOCADO SALAD

Serves 4

1 tablespoon extra virgin olive oil (or more to taste)

2 tablespoons lemon/lime juice, divided

1 tablespoon raw apple cider vinegar

¼ teaspoon sea salt

¼ teaspoon black pepper

1⅛ teaspoon garlic powder

½ English cucumber

1 orange bell pepper

1 yellow bell pepper

½ cup cilantro

1 avocado

Make the dressing by combining extra virgin olive oil, 1 tablespoon lemon juice, raw apple cider vinegar, sea salt, black pepper, and garlic powder. Set aside.

Chop the cucumber and bell peppers into medium size squares. Coarsely chop the cilantro. Combine all in medium bowl.

Slice the avocado in half and remove the seed. Scoop out the flesh and place it flat side down on a cutting board. Cut into cubes. Coat with 1 tablespoon lemon juice to prevent it from browning.

Drizzle the dressing over the vegetables. Gently fold in the avocado.

Note

You can add a tomato and onions to this recipe if you desire. Make it a main dish by adding a protein like chicken, fish, steak, or eggs and a carbohydrate like beans or chickpeas.

PEACH AND BLACK BEAN SALAD

Serves 4

2 cups cooked black beans, (or 1 BPA-free can of black beans, rinsed)

4 cups greens like spinach, kale, dark leaf lettuce, or arugula

1 red bell pepper, cut into thin strips

½ English cucumber, sliced into half circles

¼ cup sunflower seeds

1 fresh peach, cut into strips

1 tablespoon extra virgin olive oil

1½ tablespoon lemon juice

1 tablespoon raw apple cider vinegar

⅛ teaspoon sea salt

⅛ teaspoon black pepper

Combine beans, salad greens, bell pepper, cucumber, sunflower seeds, and peach strips in a medium-size bowl.

In a small bowl or glass jar, combine the olive oil, lemon juice, apple cider vinegar, sea salt, and black pepper. Drizzle over the salad.

Note

You may use different beans like garbanzo or kidney beans. You can also use a different fruit like strawberries, berries, apples, grapes, or pomegranates, depending on what's in season. You can use a different type of seed or nut like pumpkin seeds, slivered almonds, pine nuts, or walnuts.

You may add another protein source like chicken, fish, steak, or eggs to make it a main dish. Don't add more carbohydrates since it already contains beans and fruit.

MIDDLE EASTERN PARSLEY SALAD WITH TAHINI DRESSING

Serves 4

3 tomatoes

½ cucumber

1 bell pepper

2 cups parsley

¼ cup tahini sauce

3 tablespoons lemon juice

½ teaspoon sea salt

¼ teaspoon black pepper

1 tablespoon water

Dice the tomatoes, cucumber, and bell pepper. Finely chop the parsley. Combine in a bowl.

To make the dressing, combine the tahini sauce, lemon juice, salt, pepper, and water in a small bowl or glass jar or cup. Mix well until smooth.

Drizzle the dressing over the salad and toss.

Note

This salad goes well with fish and chicken. You may add a carbohydrate side to make it a main meal. Try ⅔ cup cooked quinoa.

ROASTED EGGPLANT SALAD

Serves 4

2 medium eggplants

2 tomatoes on the vine

½ bell pepper

1½ cup parsley

¼ cup pine nuts

2 tablespoons olive oil

1 tablespoon lemon juice

1 tablespoon balsamic vinegar

¼ teaspoons sea salt

¼ teaspoon black pepper

Preheat the oven or toaster oven to 350°F.

Wash the eggplants. Puncture few times with a fork or knife. Roast for 30–45 minutes until soft.

Meanwhile, chop the tomatoes, bell pepper, and parsley. Combine in a bowl with the pine nuts.

Let the eggplants cool before handling them. Peel the skin and chop the flesh. Add to the rest of the vegetables.

Make the dressing by combining the olive oil, lemon juice, balsamic vinegar, salt and pepper. Drizzle over the vegetables.

Note

If you have pomegranate molasses, you can add 1 teaspoon to this salad to give it a little bit of sweet tarty kick.

BEET AND CARROT SALAD

Serves 2

2 medium beets

4 cups spinach

1 cup shredded carrots

2 tablespoons hemp seeds

2 tablespoons extra virgin olive oil

1 tablespoon raw apple cider vinegar

1 tablespoon lemon juice

¼ teaspoon sea salt

¼ teaspoon black pepper

Wash the beets and peel them. Wear food grade gloves if you don't want your hands to turn red.

Using a spiralizer, thinly spiral the beets. If you don't have one, you can shred with a food processor, shredder, or julienne peeler. See the Zucchini noodles recipe on page 79 for ideas.

Combine the spinach, spiralized beets, carrots, and hemp seeds in a bowl.

In a glass jar or cup, mix the olive oil, vinegar, lemon, salt, and pepper.

Drizzle the dressing over the vegetables and toss.

Note

A spiralizer is a fun tool to have in you kitchen. You can buy one from Amazon at http://amzn.to/2hGGwP8.

Eat this salad with grilled chicken, coconut chicken nuggets (page 148), baked fish, or any recipe from the Protein Dishes.

Main Dish Soups and Stews

HEARTY CHICKEN VEGETABLE STEW

Serves 6

1 tablespoon extra virgin olive oil

1 small onion, finely chopped

1-inch cube fresh ginger root, finely chopped

2 garlic cloves, finely chopped

3 carrots, diced

1 zucchini, diced

2 cups sliced mushrooms

2½ cups shredded chicken (recipe on page 74 or buy a rotisserie chicken)

1½ cups white cannellini or garbanzo beans

½ teaspoon sea salt

½ teaspoon ground allspice

½ teaspoon ground cinnamon

½ teaspoon ground turmeric

¼ teaspoon ground black pepper

1½ cups chicken broth (recipe in basic recipe section)

1½ cups water

Heat the olive oil in a large stockpot. Saute the onion for 1 minute. Add the garlic and ginger and sauté for another minute.

Add the carrots, zucchini, and mushrooms and saute for 3 to 4 minutes. Add the chicken and beans.

Season with salt, allspice, cinnamon, turmeric, and black pepper and stir to coat.

Add water and chicken broth. Bring to a boil then simmer for 10 to 15 minutes.

Note

If you can't tolerate beans, remove or replace with potatoes. Wash 3 medium potatoes thoroughly and dice. Add after you saute the onion, garlic and ginger. Cook for 5-10 minutes, and then add the remaining vegetables.

TEX-MEX CHICKEN SOUP

Serves 6

1 tablespoon extra virgin olive oil

1 small onion, finely chopped

4 garlic cloves, finely chopped

1 zucchini, diced

1 yellow summer squash, diced

2 tomatoes on the vine (or plum tomatoes), diced

1–2 jalapenos, chopped

(optional)

3 raw boneless skinless chicken breasts, about 1.5 pounds

1 carton (or BPA-free can) black beans

4 cups chicken broth (homemade preferred)

1 teaspoon ground cumin

1 teaspoon paprika

½ teaspoon sea salt

½ teaspoon ground black pepper

½ teaspoon ground cinnamon

½ teaspoon coriander

2 tablespoons dried thyme

½ cup fresh cilantro, chopped

Fresh lemon or lime

2 avocados, diced (only dice what you plan to eat at a time)

Place the olive oil, onion, garlic, zucchini, summer squash, tomatoes, jalepenos, chicken breasts, beans, and chicken broth in a slow cooker.

Season with cumin, paprika, sea salt, black pepper, cinnamon, and coriander. Mix well.

Cover the slow cooker. Set on high and let it cook for 4–5 hours.

Remove the chicken breasts from the slow cooker and shred. Use forks if they are too hot to handle. Return to the soup and stir to combine. Set the slow cooker on warm.

Add the thyme and cilantro when you're almost ready to eat.

To serve, squeeze some fresh lemon or lime juice and top with some avocado pieces.

TURKEY CHILI

Serves 6-8

1 tablespoon avocado oil

1 onion, chopped

4 garlic gloves, chopped

1 pound ground lean turkey (95% lean)

1 tablespoon apple cider vinegar

3 large carrots, chopped

2 medium-large tomatoes on the vine, chopped

1 yellow bell pepper, chopped

1½ cups black beans (or 1 16-ounce BPA-free can black beans, drained and rinsed)

1½ cups red kidney beans (or 1 16-ounce BPA-free can red kidney beans, drained and rinsed)

3 tablespoons tomato paste

2 teaspoons chili powder

2 teaspoons cumin

2 teaspoons all spice

1 teaspoon salt

1 teaspoon paprika

½ teaspoon black pepper

½ teaspoon ground cinnamon

1 tablespoon dried thyme

1 teaspoon dried oregano

Optional for garnish: chopped cilantro, parsley, or scallions

In a large stockpot, heat the avocado oil and sauté the onion. After 1 minute, add the garlic.

Add the ground turkey and saute until juices run clear and no longer pink.

Add the apple cider vinegar, carrots, tomatoes, bell peppers, beans, tomato paste, chili powder, cumin, all spice, salt, paprika, black pepper, and cinnamon (all the remaining ingredients except for the dried herbs). Simmer for 1 hour on low heat.

Right before serving, add the dried thyme and oregano.

Garnish with cilantro, parsley, or scallions if desired.

Note

To make chili in the slow cooker, saute the onion, garlic, and ground turkey in a saucepan first. Transfer to a slow cooker and add remaining ingredients except for the dried herbs. Cook on low heat for 4–6 hours. Right before serving, add the dried thyme and oregano, then garnish with fresh herbs if desired.

MIDDLE EASTERN LAMB STEW WITH GREEN BEANS

Serves 4

1 tablespoon extra virgin olive oil

1 pound leg of lamb, cut into 1-inch cubes

2 teaspoons allspice, divided

1 teaspoon sea salt

1 teaspoon ground black pepper

1 teaspoon ground cinnamon

½ teaspoon ground turmeric

1 medium yellow onion, chopped

4 tomatoes on the vine, dice and reserve juice

1 pound fresh green beans, washed and cut into 2-inch strips

1 can (6 ounces) tomato paste

2 tablespoons chopped fresh cilantro

Heat the oil in a pressure cooker. Add the lamb, one teaspoon of allspice and the remaining spices. Brown. Add the onion, tomatoes with juice, and two cups warm water. Lock the pressure cooker (follow the instructions in your manual). When it starts to whistle, lower the heat to medium and cook for 12 minutes.

After 12 minutes, carefully release the pressure (follow the instructions in your manual). Add the green beans, tomato paste, one cup of water, and the remaining teaspoon of allspice. Lock the pressure cooker and cook for 2-3 minutes after it

starts whistling again. If you're not in a hurry, you can simmer for 15 minutes without pressure until the green beans are soft but still crunchy. Right before serving, mix in the chopped cilantro.

Note

Pressure cookers yield very moist lamb. If you don't have one, use a large pot or Dutch oven. It will take 30–40 minutes for the lamb pieces to cook. Traditionally, this dish is served with white rice. You can skip the rice or serve with brown rice.

Main Dish Salads

ASIAN CHICKEN COLE SLAW

Serves 4

1 English Cucumber

4 celery stalks

5 cups shredded cabbage

1 cup shredded carrots

½ cup chopped walnuts

3 tablespoons sesame seeds

2½ cups shredded chicken (see Shredded Chicken Breast in basic recipes)

2 tablespoons untoasted sesame oil, unrefined

1 tablespoon toasted sesame oil

1½ tablespoons coconut aminos (soy-free alternative) or tamari sauce (gluten-free soy sauce)

3 tablespoons apple cider vinegar

⅓ cup freshly squeezed lemon juice

½ teaspoon garlic powder, or minced small garlic clove

¼ teaspoon salt

¼ teaspoon cayenne pepper

1 teaspoon ginger powder

Cut English cucumber in half lengthwise. Thinly slice each half into half-moons. Thinly slice celery stalks. Combine cucumber, celery, shredded cabbage, walnuts, sesame seeds, and chicken in a large bowl.

In a small bowl or jar, whisk the two types of sesame oil, coconut aminos (or tamari sauce), vinegar, lemon juice, garlic, cayenne, and ginger. Drizzle the dressing over salad and serve.

Note

For short cuts, use Cole slaw cabbage mix from the produce section and rotisserie chicken or frozen pre-cooked shrimp. This salad has no carbs—have a fruit on the side or mix in diced apples, grapes, or berries. Coconut aminos is a soy-free detox alternative to soy sauce but has a milder flavor. If you prefer soy sauce, start with half the amount. Add more if needed.

GRILLED SCALLOP CITRUS SALAD

Serves 4

....

¼ cup olive oil

2 tablespoons balsamic vinegar

Zest and juice of half orange

¾ teaspoon sea salt

¼ teaspoon black pepper

1 teaspoon oregano

1 pound fresh scallops

1 onion, cut into 1-inch squares

6 cups arugula, about 10-ounce bag

6 cups baby spinach

1 cup sliced fennel bulb, about half bulb

2 tablespoons sunflower seeds

2 cups cooked quinoa

Combine the olive oil, balsamic vinegar, orange juice and zest, salt, pepper, and oregano in a small bowl or glass jar. Stir well.

Place the scallops and onion squares in a bowl. Drizzle half the dressing and gently toss.

Prepare the skewers. Insert a scallop then an onion square in a wooden skewer. Repeat 2-3 times. Each skewer should have 3-4 scallops.

Turn on the grill on medium heat. Place the skewers on the grill and cook for 3 minutes.

Turn a quarter turn every 3 minutes. The scallops will be cooked when they turn pink.

Combine the arugula, spinach, sliced fennel, sunflower seeds, and cooked quinoa in a large bowl. Toss with the remaining dressing. Divide into 4 plates or bowls. Divide the scallops among the bowls. Enjoy.

Note:
If you don't have a grill, see page 151 for instructions on how to cook scallops on the stove.

TUNA AVOCADO SALAD

Serves 2

1 avocado

2 tablespoons lemon juice

2 4-ounce cans light chunk tuna packed in water, drained

2 tablespoons sunflower seeds (or pumpkin, or slivered almonds)

1 tomato on the vine, chopped

A dash of ground black pepper

A dash of garlic powder

In a small bowl, mash the avocado with a fork. Immediately drizzle with lemon juice.

Drain liquid from the tuna. Add the tuna, sunflower seeds, tomatoes, black pepper, and garlic powder to the avocado. Fold gently.

Serve as is or scooped with endive lettuce or celery sticks.

Note

This recipe contains no carbohydrate. Eat a piece of fruit with this meal.

You can also use apple slices to scoop up some salad. Alternatively, you can mix in sliced grapes or berries.

POMEGRANATE TUNA SALAD

Serves 2

1 tablespoon extra virgin olive oil

1 tablespoon freshly squeezed lemon juice

1 tablespoon raw apple cider vinegar

1 teaspoon yellow or spicy mustard

¼ teaspoon sea salt

¼ teaspoon ground black pepper

¼ teaspoon garlic powder

1 teaspoon dried oregano

1 avocado

2 4-ounce cans light chunk tuna packed in water, drained

4 cups baby spinach

½ English cucumber, diced

1 yellow bell pepper

1 cup pomegranate seeds

Make the dressing first by combining olive oil, lemon juice, vinegar, mustard, salt, pepper, garlic, and oregano in a glass jar.

In a small bowl, mash the avocado. Fold in the tuna. Drizzle half the dressing amount, making sure the avocado in completely coated.

In a separate bowl, combine the spinach, cucumber, and bell pepper. Toss with the remaining dressing.

To serve, place spinach and vegetables in two shallow serving bowls or plates. Top each bowl with half the amount of tuna. Divide the pomegranate seeds between the two plates.

Note

Pomegranate is a delicious antioxidant-rich fruit in season in the fall and winter. In the spring and summer, or if you can't find pomegranate, try blueberries or red grapes instead.

SHRIMP DETOX SALAD

Serves 4

1 pound pre-cooked shrimp, tail off (if using frozen shrimp, thaw completely)

3 cups chopped fresh Kale

1½ cups shredded green cabbage

1½ cups shredded red cabbage

1 cup shredded carrots

¼ cup sunflower seeds

3 tablespoons olive oil

1 tablespoon lemon juice (roughly half a lemon)

1 tablespoon apple cider vinegar

1 tablespoon spicy brown mustard

¼ teaspoon sea salt

¼ teaspoon black pepper

Optional: 1 cup quinoa or beans

If using frozen shrimp, thaw according to package instructions, 20-30 minutes in advance.

In a medium bowl, combine the kale, cabbage, carrots, and sunflower seeds.

In a small jar or glass, combine the olive oil, lemon juice, vinegar, mustard, salt, and pepper.

Drizzle the dressing over the vegetables and toss, making sure all greens are coated.

Add the shrimp and toss.

Note

Without the quinoa or beans, this dish is low in carbohydrates. If you're active or have just worked out, you need the carbs. If you don't like or can't tolerate beans or quinoa, have a piece of fruit on the side.

BEEF TACO SALAD

Serves 4

FOR THE BEEF:

1 tablespoon olive oil

1 pound 95% lean ground beef

2–3 garlic cloves, finely chopped

1 small onion, finely chopped

1 teaspoon chili powder

1 teaspoon cumin

½ teaspoon salt

½ teaspoon coriander

½ teaspoon oregano

¼ teaspoon paprika

FOR THE DRESSING:

¼ cup extra virgin olive oil

2 tablespoons raw apple cider vinegar

1 lime, juices

½ teaspoon sea salt

¼ teaspoon coriander

¼ teaspoon chili powder

¼ teaspoon garlic

FOR THE SALAD:

8 cups salad greens (lettuce, spinach, arugula, kale, etc.), chopped

1 cup sliced olives

3 tomatoes on the vine, chopped

1 avocado, cubed or sliced

Optional: 1 cup black beans (or 1 BPA-free can of black beans, rinsed)

In a medium saucepan, heat the olive oil. Brown the ground beef until no longer pink. Add the onion and garlic. Continue to sauté for 2–3 minutes. Add all beef seasonings and let it cook for 5–10 minutes.

Meanwhile, make the salad dressing. Combine oil, vinegar, juice of 1 lime, sea salt, coriander, chili powder, and garlic in a jar. Shake well. Set aside.

In a large serving bowl, combine salad greens, olives, and tomatoes. Top with the cooked beef, avocado cubes, and black beans. Drizzle the dressing and toss.

Vegetable Dishes

EGGPLANT AND ZUCCHINI RATATOUILLE

Serves 4

2 garlic cloves, finely chopped

1 large eggplant

3 medium zucchini

1 tablespoon extra virgin olive oil

3 tomatoes on the vine, diced

½ teaspoon salt

¼ teaspoon black pepper

1 teaspoon dried oregano

1 teaspoon dried and crushed thyme

Wash the zucchini and eggplant thoroughly and chop them into ½-inch chunks.

Heat the oil in a large sauté pan over medium heat. Add the garlic, zucchini and eggplant, and sauté for 2–3 minutes.

Add the tomatoes with their juice, salt, black pepper, oregano, and crushed thyme. Lower the temperature, and simmer for 20 minutes or until the vegetables are soft.

Note

Serve with a protein dish and a carbohydrate dish. See the Protein Dishes and Carbohydrate Dishes for options.

ROASTED PEPPERS AND MUSHROOMS

Serves 4

3 bell peppers of different colors (green, orange, red, and yellow), cut into 1-inch squares

1 container (10-ounces) baby bella mushroom,

washed and cut in half

1 small onion, cut into 1-inch squares

1 tablespoon extra virgin olive or avocado oil

1 tablespoon oregano

1 tablespoon basil

½ tablespoon thyme

½ teaspoon sea salt

½ teaspoon black pepper

Preheat the oven to 375°F.

Prepare the peppers, mushroom, and onion. Place on a medium-size baking sheet.

Drizzle the oil over the veggies. Season with the herbs, salt, and pepper. Make sure all the vegetables are coated.

Roast in the oven for 30 minutes, or until they reach desired texture.

Note

Serve with a protein dish and a carbohydrate dish. See the Protein Dishes and Carbohydrate Dishes for options.

SAUTÉED COLORFUL CABBAGE

Serves 4

½ head green cabbage

½ head red cabbage

1 tablespoon olive oil

1 inch fresh ginger root, peeled and chopped

1 tablespoon apple cider vinegar

3 tablespoons cilantro, chopped

1 tablespoon sesame seeds

Salt and pepper to taste

Remove the outer leaves from each cabbage. Cut each one in half.

Place the half cabbage on a cutting board flat side down. Using a large knife, shred into about 1 inch pieces. Wash with cold water. Let is sit for 10 minutes.

In a large pot, heat the olive oil on medium heat. Add the ginger and sauté for 1 minute.

Toss in the cabbage and apple cider vinegar. Cover and let it cook for 5 minutes.

Remove from the heat. Season with salt and pepper to taste. Add the cilantro and sesame seeds. The cabbage will be slightly crunchy but that's on purpose to preserve its health benefits.

Note

Serve with a protein dish and a carbohydrate dish. See the Protein Dishes and Carbohydrate Dishes for options.

ROASTED BRUSSELS SPROUTS

Serves 4

1 pound fresh Brussels
    sprouts

1 tablespoon avocado oil

¼ teaspoon ground garlic

¼ teaspoon sea salt

¼ teaspoon ground black
    pepper

Juice of 1 lemon or 1
    tablespoon raw apple
    cider vinegar

Preheat the oven to 400°F.

Wash the Brussels sprouts and remove the outer brown leaves. You can cut them in half if you like or keep them whole. Place them on a baking sheet.

Drizzle the avocado oil over the Brussels sprouts. Toss and make sure they are evenly coated. Roast in the oven for 30–40 minutes.

In a small cup, combine the garlic, salt, pepper, and lemon juice or vinegar.

Transfer the Brussels sprouts to a serving bowl when done roasting. Drizzle with the lemon sauce and toss.

Serve immediately.

Note

Serve with a protein dish and a carbohydrate dish. See the Protein Dishes and Carbohydrate Dishes for options.

MASHED CAULIFLOWER

Serves 4

1 head cauliflower

6 medium garlic cloves, unpeeled

1 teaspoon + 1 tablespoon extra virgin olive oil or unrefined coconut oil

¼ teaspoon sea salt

¼ teaspoon ground black pepper

Preheat the oven (or a small toaster oven) to 400°F.

Remove the leaves of the cauliflower. Cut off the florets from the stem and wash.

Place a steamer basket in a stainless steel pot. Add enough water so that it doesn't touch the cauliflower. Place the cauliflower in the basket, cover, and steam for 10–20 minutes or until very soft.

Meanwhile, cut off the tips of the garlic cloves. You don't need to peel them completely. Place them on a foil paper and drizzle with 1 teaspoon of olive oil. Fold the foil paper so that it completely encloses the garlic. Roast them in the oven for 20 minutes. Peel after they are roasted.

Use a fork to check on the cauliflower. When soft, remove from the pot. Remove the steamer basket and discard the water.

Add the cauliflower and roasted garlic back in the pot. Add the remaining tablespoon of olive oil, salt, and pepper.

Using a hand-held blender, puree the cauliflower until soft and smooth.

Serve warm.

Note

If you don't have a hand-held blender, use a regular blender, food processor, or masher. If you use coconut oil, you will get a very nice coconut flavor. If you need more liquid, you can add 2 tablespoons canned coconut milk.

You can make the roasted garlic few days in advance, especially if you're turning the oven on to roast or bake something else.

SAUTÉED COLLARD GREENS

Serves 2

....

1 bunch collard greens, organic preferably

1 tablespoon extra virgin olive oil

1 small onion, finely chopped

2 garlic cloves, finely chopped

¼ teaspoon salt

½ teaspoon black pepper

1 tablespoon fresh lemon juice (about half a fresh lemon), or more as desired

Wash the collard greens and pat dry with a paper towel. Cut the hard white stems in the middle with a knife or with your hands. If using your hands, hold the stem in one hand and then slide your other hand over the leaf and snap it from the stem. Stack the leaves on top of each other. Gather into a bundle and chop.

Place the collard greens in a medium-large saute pot. Add as little water as possible just to cover the greens. Cover with a lid. Simmer for 5 minutes on low heat.

Strain the collard greens. Reserve the water and add it to soups and stews.

In the same pot on medium heat, add the olive oil and saute the onion for 1 minute. Add the garlic and saute for another minute.

Stir in the cooked collard greens. Season with salt and pepper. Combine well.

Remove from the heat and drizzle with lemon juice.

Serve warm.

Note

You can use this recipe to cook other greens like kale, mustard greens, Swiss chard, or dandelion greens. Serve with a protein dish and a carbohydrate dish. See the Protein Dishes and Carbohydrate Dishes for options.

VEGETABLE STUFFED PORTOBELLO MUSHROOM

Serves 4–6

- 6 portobello mushrooms, rinsed quickly in cold water
- ¼ cup extra virgin olive oil
- 2 tablespoons balsamic vinegar
- ¼ teaspoon sea salt
- ¼ teaspoon ground black pepper
- 4 garlic cloves, mined
- 1 small yellow onion, chopped
- 4 cups packed spinach leaves, washed and chopped
- 2 tomatoes on the vine, chopped
- 1 tablespoon dried thyme or oregano
- Additional salt and pepper, about ¼ teaspoon each

Preheat the oven to 400°F.

Remove mushroom stems. Chop and reserve.

Combine the olive oil, balsamic vinegar, ¼ teaspoon sea salt, ¼ teaspoon black pepper, and half the garlic amount in a small bowl. Brush the top and bottom of the mushrooms with the oil mix and place on a baking sheet with a rim (or baking dish). Bake for 5 minutes.

Meanwhile, combine the chopped mushroom stems, onion, remaining garlic, spinach, tomatoes, thyme, and additional salt and pepper. Fill mushroom caps with the stuffing. Bake for 10 minutes.

Serve warm.

Note

Don't soak mushrooms in water. That will make them soggy. Reserve the juices that remain in the baking dish and use as sauce or to make gravy. Try this recipe with grilled fish or chicken and pour the juices from the mushroom and vegetables over the protein to make it moist.

ROASTED ASPARAGUS

Serves 4

....

1 bunch asparagus

1 tablespoon extra virgin olive oil

¼ teaspoon sea salt

¼ teaspoon ground black pepper

¼ teaspoon garlic powder

Juice of 1 lemon

Wash the asparagus stems. Holding each stem with both hands, snap at about 2 inches from the bottom, removing about a quarter of the stem. This will remove the chewy stringy part of the stems.

Place on a baking sheet. Drizzle the olive oil and season with salt, pepper, and garlic powder. Roast for 10–15 minutes.

Drizzle the lemon juice when done cooking.

Note

Serve with a protein dish and a carbohydrate dish. See the Protein Dishes and Carbohydrate Dishes for options.

ROASTED TURMERIC CAULIFLOWER

Serve 4

....

1 head cauliflower

3 tablespoons avocado or coconut oil

¾ teaspoon ground turmeric

¾ teaspoon garlic powder

¾ teaspoon sea salt

½ teaspoon black pepper

2–3 tablespoons lemon juice

Preheat the oven to 400°F.

Cut the cauliflower head into florets of similar sizes. Wash and pat dry with a paper towel. Place on a baking sheet. Drizzle the oil and season with turmeric, garlic powder, salt and pepper. Make sure all florets are coated.

Roast in the oven for 35–40 minutes.

When done, place in a large bowl and toss with lemon juice.

Serve warm.

Note

Serve with a protein dish and a carbohydrate dish. See the Protein Dishes and Carbohydrate Dishes for options.

GRILLED ZUCCHINI

Serves 2

2 medium zucchinis

1 tablespoon extra virgin olive oil

¼ teaspoon sea salt

¼ teaspoon black pepper

¼ teaspoon garlic powder

¼ teaspoon paprika

½ teaspoon dried oregano

Turn the grill on medium-high.

Cut each zucchini lengthwise in thirds, about ½-inch thick. Place on a flat plate or cutting board.

Drizzle the olive oil over the zucchini slices and season with salt, pepper, garlic, paprika, and oregano. You can use a cooking brush to make sure spices are evenly spread.

Place on the grill. Grill for 4–5 minutes on each side.

Note

You can make this recipe on an indoor griddle or even roasted in the oven. Serve with a protein dish and a carbohydrate dish. See the Protein Dishes and Carbohydrate Dishes for options.

Protein Dishes

FIVE HERB CHICKEN

Serves 6

2 teaspoons dried sage

1 teaspoon dried oregano

1 teaspoon dried thyme

1 teaspoon dried rosemary

1 teaspoon dried basil

1 teaspoon sea salt

1 teaspoon ground black pepper

2 tablespoons extra virgin olive oil

2 pounds chicken breasts

Preheat the oven to 375°F.

Combine the sage, oregano, thyme, rosemary, basil, salt, pepper, and olive oil in a small bowl. Let it sit for 2–5 minutes.

Meanwhile, place the chicken breasts on a baking dish.

Drizzle the spice and oil mix over the chicken. Rub with your hands and make sure all the chicken is covered.

Bake for 1 hour. Insert a food thermometer in the chicken breasts and make sure they reached 165°F. Don't overcook.

Note

It's important to cook chicken well. However, if overcooked, it will become dry and unappealing. We found that the best way to cook chicken, and proteins in general, is to use a food thermometer.

You may use this recipe with a whole chicken. Serve with a side salad or cooked vegetables and a side of carbohydrates like sweet potatoes.

CHICKEN WITH HERBED TOMATOES AND MUSHROOMS

Serves 6

FOR THE CHICKEN:

2 pounds boneless skinless chicken breasts, halved

2 tablespoons extra virgin olive oil

¼ teaspoon sea salt

½ teaspoon ground black pepper

1 teaspoon dried rosemary, chopped

1 teaspoon dried basil

1 teaspoon dried oregano

1 teaspoon dried thyme

FOR THE HERBED TOMATOES AND MUSHROOMS

1 tablespoon extra virgin olive oil

1 medium red onion, chopped

2 medium garlic cloves, finely chopped

3 cups grape tomatoes, cut in half

2 cups sliced mushrooms

¼ teaspoon sea salt

¼ teaspoon ground black pepper

1 teaspoon dried oregano

1 teaspoon dried thyme

½ cup fresh parsley, chopped

Preheat the oven to 375°F.

Place the chicken pieces in a freezer bag. Using a pestle or wooden spoon, pound the breasts so that they all have the same thickness. Add 2 tablespoons olive oil, salt, black pepper, rosemary, basil, oregano, and thyme to the plastic bag. Seal the bag. Shake and rotate to make sure all pieces are coated.

Prepare the tomato herb sauce. In the same skillet on medium heat, pour 1 tablespoon olive oil. Add the chopped onion and garlic and saute for 1 minute. Add the tomatoes, mushrooms, sea salt, black pepper, dried oregano, and dried thyme. Saute for 3–4 minutes.

Heat a skillet on medium heat. Add the chicken pieces, one at a time, and sear for about 2 minutes on each side, until the chicken looks golden. Transfer to a baking dish. Prepare the tomato herb sauce. In the same skillet on medium heat, pour 1 tablespoon olive oil. Add the chopped onion and garlic and saute for 1 minute. Add the tomatoes, mushrooms, sea salt, black pepper, dried oregano, and dried thyme. Saute for 3–4 minutes.

Pour the tomato sauce over the chicken. Sprinkle fresh parsley on top. Bake for 30 minutes, until the chicken is completely cooked. Insert a food thermometer in the chicken breasts and make sure they reached 165°F. Don't overcook.

Note

You can marinate the chicken in the seasonings in the fridge overnight. You can replace the mushrooms with asparagus or green beans.

GRILLED CHICKEN KEBABS

Serves 4

1½ pounds chicken breasts

4 garlic cloves, chopped

1 tablespoon chopped fresh ginger, about ½ inch cube

½ teaspoon paprika

½ teaspoon ground black pepper

¼ teaspoon sea salt

¼ teaspoon turmeric

2 tablespoons avocado oil

3 tablespoons fresh lemon juice

2 bell peppers, any colors

Cut the chicken breasts into 1-inch cubes. Place in a bowl or freezer bag.

Add the garlic, ginger, paprika, black pepper, sea salt, turmeric, avocado oil, and lemon juice. Seal the bag and combine, making sure all chicken pieces are coated well. Marinate in the fridge for at least 1 hour.

Cut the bell peppers into 1-inch squares.

Place wooden skewers in a 9 x 13 pan. Soak in water to soften them and prevent splintering.

Skewer the chicken and peppers, alternating between one another.

Turn the grill on high. Place the skewers on the grill. Rotate the skewer a quarter turn every 3–4 minutes. Insert a food thermometer in the chicken pieces and make sure they reached 165°F. The chicken is cooked when the outside is golden brown and the inside is no longer pink. Do not char.

Note

You can grill many vegetables in the same chicken skewers or separately. Try green peppers, mushrooms, tomatoes, onion, or zucchini rings. Serve with a side salad or cooked vegetables and a side of carbohydrates like sweet potatoes.

YELLOW CHICKEN WITH AVOCADO DRESSING

Serves 4

....

1 pound chicken breasts, cut into tenders

2 tablespoons avocado oil

1 tablespoon spicy brown mustard

1 tablespoon apple cider vinegar

2 garlic cloves, minced

¼ teaspoon sea salt

1 tablespoon thyme

¼ teaspoon turmeric

1 avocado

2 tablespoons lemon juice

¼ teaspoon salt

Place the chicken in a bowl or re-sealable bag. Add the avocado oil, mustard, apple cider vinegar, garlic cloves, salt, thyme, and turmeric. Seal the bag and combine making sure the chicken is coated well. Marinate for 2–3 hours in the fridge or overnight.

Heat a large skillet for 1 minute on medium-hot. Add the chicken tenders with the marinade. Cook on one side covered until golden. Turn on the other side and brown covered until the chicken is completely cooked. You can use a thermometer to check the chicken temperature.

Meanwhile, mash the avocado until very smooth. Combine with 2 tablespoons lemon juice and ¼ teaspoon salt. Serve over the chicken.

Note

You can use the seasonings in this recipe and grill the chicken instead of cooking in a skillet. Keep them whole or cut them into 1-inch cubes and skewer.

Serve this recipe with a side salad or cooked vegetables and a side of carbohydrates like sweet potatoes.

COCONUT CHICKEN NUGGETS WITH SPICY HONEY MUSTARD SAUCE

Serves 4

FOR THE CHICKEN

1 large egg

2 tablespoons water

6 tablespoons coconut flour

1 teaspoon sea salt

½ teaspoon ground black pepper

1 teaspoon turmeric powder

2 teaspoon dried oregano

1½ pounds chicken breast, cut into 1-inch cubes

FOR THE SAUCE

¼ cup yellow mustard

1 tablespoon honey

2 tablespoons srirachia sauce (optional)

¼ teaspoon sea salt

1 tablespoon lemon juice

Preheat the oven to 400°F.

In a medium bowl, whisk the egg with water. Set aside. In a second bowl, combine the coconut flour, salt, black pepper, and oregano.

Dredge the chicken pieces, one or few at a time, in the egg mixture. Pull out quickly. Then roll in the coconut flour mixture. Place on a baking sheet. Continue with all pieces.

Bake for 20 minutes.

Meanwhile, combine the mustard, honey, srirachia sauce, and salt in a small pot. Bring to a boil and cook for 1–2 minutes. Let it cool and serve at room temperature when the chicken is cooked.

Note

Serve with a side salad or cooked vegetables and a side of carbohydrates like baked potatoes.

BASIC BROILED SALMON

Serves 4

....

1 pound wild-caught salmon
    fillets

½ teaspoon ground cumin

½ teaspoon ground
    coriander

½ teaspoon dried oregano

½ teaspoon dried thyme

½ teaspoon ground black
    pepper

¼ teaspoon sea salt

1 tablespoon extra virgin
    olive oil

Juice of 1 lemon

Preheat the oven to 400°F. Place a piece of parchment paper on a baking tray.

Place salmon fillets on the parchment paper.

Combine cumin, coriander, oregano, thyme, black pepper, salt and olive oil in a small bowl. Rub over the salmon.

Bake for 15–20 minutes. The fish is done when it can easily flake with a fork.

Drizzle lemon juice over the salmon right before serving.

Note

Do not overcook the salmon because it will dry out. Thicker pieces of salmon need more time to cook. Using a food thermometer, cook fish to 135°F. Serve with a side salad or cooked vegetables and a side of carbohydrates like cooked quinoa.

ZESTY HERBED SALMON

Serves 4

....

1 pound wild-caught salmon
   fillets

1 tablespoon fresh parsley

½ teaspoon brown spicy
   mustard

1 tablespoon balsamic

vinegar

½ teaspoon dried oregano

½ teaspoon dried basil

½ teaspoon ground black
   pepper

¼ teaspoon sea salt

¼ teaspoon garlic powder

1 tablespoon extra virgin
   olive oil

Juice of 1 lemon

Preheat the oven to 400°F. Place a piece of
parchment paper on a baking tray.

Place salmon fillets on the parchment paper.

Combine the parsley, mustard, balsamic
vinegar, oregano, basil, black pepper, salt,
garlic and olive oil in a small bowl. Rub over
the salmon.

Bake for 15–20 minutes. You know the fish
is done when it can easily flake with a fork.

Drizzle lemon juice over the salmon right
before serving.

Note

*Do not overcook the salmon because
it will dry out. Thicker pieces of salmon
need more time to cook. Using a food
thermometer, cook fish to 135°F. Serve with
a side salad or cooked vegetables and a
side of carbohydrates like cooked quinoa or
Creamy Red Potato Salad.*

PAN-SEARED SCALLOPS

Serves 4

....

½ tablespoon + ¼ cup avocado oil

1 pound scallops, washed and patted dry (if frozen, thaw completely)

¼ cup freshly squeezed lemon juice, about 1 small lemon

4 garlic cloves, finely chopped

½ tablespoon finely chopped chives

¼ teaspoon sea salt

¼ teaspoon ground black pepper

Heat ½ tablespoon avocado oil in a saute pan on high, preferably a cast iron skillet. Meanwhile, pat the scallops dry with a paper towel.

Place scallops in one layer in the pan. Let them cook until they get golden brown, about 5 minutes. Turn them over to cook on the other side for 3 to 5 minutes.

Remove from the pan and place in a shallow bowl for serving.

Remove any charred scallop remnants from the pan.

Place ¼ cup avocado oil, lemon juice, garlic, chives, salt, and pepper in the same pan. Sauté for 1 minute until the garlic becomes golden brown. Pour over the scallops and serve immediately

Note

To make a complete meal, serve with a side salad or cooked vegetables and a carbohydrate dish. Try the Quinoa Vegetable Pilaf on page. If you want a low carb meal, serve it with zucchini noodles (page 79).

If you're not a fan of scallops, you can use shrimp. You can replace the chives with parsley, cilantro, basil, or dill.

Cook the scallops with avocado oil because it tolerates higher heat better than olive oil. You can also use coconut oil.

LEMON GARLIC SHRIMP

Serves 4

....

1 pound shrimp, fresh or frozen (cooked or uncooked)

4 tablespoons extra virgin olive oil, divided

½ onion, finely chopped

2 garlic cloves, finely chopped

¼ teaspoon sea salt

¼ teaspoon black pepper

¼ teaspoon paprika

¼ cup chopped parsley

Juice of ½ lemon

If starting with raw shrimp, devein by cutting through the back and removing the black vein. Remove the tail. If using frozen (raw or cooked) shrimp, soak in warm water for 30 minutes first. Remove the tail.

Heat 2 tablespoons olive oil in medium-size saucepan on medium heat. Saute the onion and garlic until translucent.

Add the shrimp, salt, pepper, and paprika. If the shrimp is raw, cook until they turn pink. If it's pre-cooked shrimp, saute until warm. Pre-cooked shrimp needs less time so make sure you don't overcook it.

Add parsley, lemon, and 2 more tablespoons of olive oil. Cook for 1 minute until everything is combined. If you prefer more sauce, add a little bit of water and adjust the salt, pepper, and lemon if needed.

Note

Serve with your favorite vegetable from the Vegetable Dishes and a carbohydrate like spaghetti squash from the Carbohydrate Dishes.

PECAN CRUSTED FLOUNDER

Serves 4

....

1 cup pecans

¼ teaspoon garlic powder

½ teaspoon dry mustard powder

2 tablespoon coconut milk

2 tablespoons coconut flour

¼ teaspoon cayenne pepper

½ teaspoon salt

4 flounder fillets, 4 ounces each

Preheat the oven to 400°F. Place a piece of parchment paper on a baking tray.

Chop the pecans using a large knife, or food processor. Do not over process—keep them coarse.

In a bowl, combine the pecans, garlic, mustard, coconut milk, coconut flour, cayenne pepper, and salt.

Place founder fillets on the baking sheet. Press ¼ of the nut mixture on each fillet.

Bake in the oven for 15 minutes or until the

fish flakes easily with a fork.

Note

You can use other types of white fish like mahimahi, snapper, or trout. Serve with steamed or roasted vegetables like asparagus and beets. Beets make a very nutrient-rich carbohydrate.

TOMATO OLIVE BAKED COD

Serves 6

....

2 pounds cod fillets

½ small red onion, diced

4 garlic cloves, diced

½ teaspoon salt

¼ teaspoon black pepper

½ teaspoon dried basil

½ teaspoon dried oregano

¼ cup pitted and sliced green olives

2 cups fresh tomatoes, diced (tomatoes on the vine are best. May replace with a 28-ounce BPA-free can of diced tomatoes)

½ teaspoon apple cider vinegar

Preheat the oven to 350°F.

Place cod on a baking sheet with rim.

Combine all the remaining ingredients in a medium size bowl. Place on top of the cod fillets.

Bake for 20 minutes or until the fish flakes easily with a fork.

Note

Serve with steamed green beans or collard greens and a side of quinoa or rice.

Carbohydrate Dishes

ROASTED SPAGHETTI SQUASH

Serves 6

....

1 spaghetti squash

1 tablespoon extra virgin olive oil, coconut oil, or avocado oil

½ teaspoon sea salt

¼ teaspoon ground black pepper

2 teaspoons fresh herbs like parsley, cilantro, chives, or scallions (optional)

Preheat the oven to 400°F.

Cut spaghetti squash lengthwise in half. Remove the seeds with a spoon. You may wash them and roast them separately.

Place the squash with the pulp down on a baking tray with a rim. Add some water, about ¼ cup.

Roast for 45 minutes or until the pulp is soft and comes out easily looking like spaghetti with a fork. Continue to fork.

Place the spaghetti squash in a large bowl. Toss with oil, salt, and pepper. Garnish with fresh herbs.

Note

Spaghetti squash is a starchy vegetable that can easily replace pastas and rice while boosting your meal with vitamins and minerals. Baking with the pulp down will help it stay moist.

CREAMY RED POTATO SALAD

Serves 6

....

**2 pounds red potatoes with
   skin, washed and cubed**

**4 garlic cloves, minced with
   a mortar and pestle**

2 tablespoons yellow

mustard

¼ cup extra virgin olive oil

1 tablespoon coconut milk

½ teaspoon sea salt

¼ teaspoon ground black

pepper

1 red bell pepper, chopped

2 celery stalks, sliced

**3 tablespoons chopped
   chives**

Place the potatoes in a large pot. Cover with cold water and boil for 10 minutes or until soft but not overcooked. Drain and place in a large bowl. Let them cool.

While the potatoes boil, make the dressing. Whisk the garlic, mustard, olive oil, coconut milk, salt and pepper in a small bowl.

When the potatoes reach room temperature, add the red bell pepper, celery, and chives. Drizzle the dressing over the vegetables and fold with a spatula slowly until all

ingredients are combined.

Refrigerate for 2–4 hours before serving for flavors to combine.

Note:
This recipe goes well with grilled chicken, coconut chicken nuggets, or baked fish. Make sure you have a non-starchy salad on the side as well. Keep the potato skin because it contains more fiber.

HERB RED POTATOES

Serves 4

4 small potatoes

2 tablespoons avocado oil

¼ teaspoon sea salt

¼ teaspoon garlic powder

¼ teaspoon paprika

¼ teaspoon dried oregano

¼ teaspoon dried basil

Dash of ground black pepper

Preheat the oven to 350°F.

Thoroughly scrub the potatoes with a vegetable brush. Cut into ½-inch cubes. Place on a baking sheet.

Drizzle the avocado oil over the potatoes. Sprinkle all seasonings. Using a brush or your hand, make sure all potato pieces are coated.

Cover with foil paper and bake for 30 minutes.

Remove the foil paper and bake for another 15 minutes or until they reach desired texture.

Note

Covering the potatoes initially helps them cook completely without getting burnt or dried out. Serve with a protein dish like Coconut Chicken Nuggets and a vegetables dish like the Fennel Arugula Salad.

QUINOA VEGETABLE PILAF

Serves 4

1 cup dry quinoa

2 cups water

1 tablespoon extra virgin olive oil

½ small onion, chopped

2 garlic cloves

½ inch cube fresh ginger root, chopped

1 cup shredded carrots

2 cups shredded cabbage

½ tablespoon raw apple cider vinegar

½ teaspoon salt

¼ teaspoon black pepper

½ cup slivered almonds

2 cups packed baby spinach, chopped

Rinse the quinoa thoroughly with water then drain. If your strainer is too large, place a paper towel inside of it to collect the quinoa.

Place the quinoa and water in a medium saucepan and bring to a boil. Simmer covered for 15 minutes. Quinoa is done when translucent and flakes. Remove from the pan.

Heat the olive oil on medium heat in the same pan. Saute the onions until translucent for about 2 minutes. Add the ginger and garlic and cook for another minute. Stir in the shredded carrots and cabbage, the apple cider vinegar, salt, and pepper. Cook for 5 minutes, stirring it few times.

Add the cooked quinoa, almonds and spinach. Cook for 5 more minutes. Check the seasonings and adjust if needed.

Serve warm.

Note

Consider this your vegetable and carbohydrate for the meal. Despite having more protein than other grains, quinoa is still heavy on carbs. You might need animal proteins to feel satisfied without overeating quinoa. Serve with 1–2 boiled eggs or 2–3 ounces leftover chicken, turkey, smoked salmon, or cocktail shrimp.

3-in-1 Meals

BEEF VEGETABLE STIR-FRY

Serves 4

- 1 pound grass-fed beef for stir-frying
- 2 tablespoons flax meal
- 3 garlic cloves, peeled and minced
- 1-inch cube fresh ginger, peeled and minced
- 1 tablespoons coconut oil, divided
- 6 cups stir-fry vegetables (carrot slices, bell pepper squares, broccoli florets, bok choy leaves)
- ½ cup chicken broth
- 2 tablespoons coconut aminos (or gluten-free tamari sauce)
- ¼ cup fresh lemon juice
- 1 teaspoon honey
- 2 scallions, chopped
- Sesame seeds (optional)
- Red hot pepper flakes (optional)

Trim the fat from the meat and slice into thick strips. Place in a bowl and toss with flax meal. Set aside. Chop the vegetables.

Heat 1 tablespoon of coconut oil on medium heat in a wok. Saute the garlic and ginger for 30 seconds. Add the beef and saute until no longer pink, about 1–2 minutes. Remove and set aside.

Heat the remaining tablespoon of coconut oil and saute the vegetables. If using carrots and broccoli, saute them first for 2 minutes before adding peppers, mushrooms, or bok choy.

Meanwhile, combine chicken broth, coconut aminos, lemon juice, and honey in a glass jar or cup.

Add the beef back to the vegetables. Pour the sauce over. Cook for 2–3 minutes.

Mix in half the chopped scallions. Keep the remaining scallion for garnish with sesame seeds and red hot pepper flakes.

Note

If you don't have flax meal, toss the beef with rice or coconut flour. It gives a nice texture to the beef but can be skipped completely if needed.

Coconut aminos is soy-free alternative to soy sauce that I recommend as part of a detox plan. If you prefer soy sauce or gluten-free tamari sauce, start with half the amount first and add more if needed because they have more sodium and a stronger flavor.

CHICKEN AND GREENS OVER SWEET POTATOES

Serves 4

2 medium sweet potatoes

1 tablespoon extra virgin olive oil

1 pound chicken breasts

½ onion, diced

2 garlic cloves, chopped

3 cups cabbage (mixed color is better), chopped

1 cup shredded carrots

4 cups kale, chopped

½ teaspoon sea salt

½ teaspoon turmeric

¼ teaspoon black pepper

1 cup chicken broth (will make from chicken)

¼ cup packed parsley, chopped

2 tablespoons sunflower seeds

Heat the oven to 375°F. Wash the potatoes thoroughly with a vegetable brush to remove any dirt. Cut any bruised parts and pierce all around with a knife. Wrap the potatoes with a large piece of foil paper and bake in the oven for 45 minutes. They are done when you can insert a knife in the potatoes and pull it back easily.

While the potatoes cook, place the chicken breasts in a medium size pot. Sprinkle some salt and pepper. Cover with water and boil for 15–20 minutes until no longer pink. Remove the chicken breasts from the water and place on a plate. Reserve the stock. Shred the chicken using two forks or with your hands.

In the same pot, heat the tablespoon of olive oil. Add onion and garlic and saute for 1–2 minutes. Add cabbage, carrots, kale, salt, turmeric, pepper, and chicken broth (or water). Cook for 10–15 minutes until soft but still crunchy.

Remove the vegetables from the heat and mix in the shredded chicken, parsley, and sunflower seeds.

To serve, place ½ sweet potato in each plate. Top with the amount of the chicken and vegetables.

Note

To prepare in advance (perfect for a weekday dinner): on the weekend, bake the sweet potatoes and store in a container. Cook, shred, and store the chicken in another container. Store the stock in a glass jar. Store all ingredients in the fridge. To assemble, reheat the potatoes in the oven for 15 minutes and add the chicken earlier with the vegetables so they get warm.

Do no overcook the cabbage to preserve its nutrient and antioxidant content. Adding the parsley and sunflower seeds after turning off the heat helps preserve nutrients as well.

DETOX SHEPPARD'S PIE

Serves 8

2 cauliflower heads

½ cup canned coconut milk

½ teaspoon sea salt

½ tablespoon coconut oil

1 medium onion, chopped

4 garlic cloves, chopped

1 pound lean ground turkey or chicken

3 cups chopped broccoli florets, about 1 head

4 cups fresh chopped kale leaves, about 4 large stalks

4 carrots, diced (about 1 cup)

1 cup frozen green peas

1 teaspoon sea salt

¼ teaspoon cayenne pepper

½ teaspoon cinnamon

½ teaspoon turmeric

Remove the outer leaves of the cauliflower. Cut into florets and wash. Place in a large pot and cover with water. Cook until soft, about 30 minutes. Drain the water.

Add the coconut milk and half a teaspoon sea salt to the cauliflower. Puree with a handheld blender or masher. Remove from the pot.

Preheat the oven to 400°F.

In the same pot, heat the coconut oil. Saute the onion and garlic until soft. Add ground turkey and brown until juices run clear. Add the broccoli, carrots, kale, green peas, one teaspoon salt, cayenne pepper, cinnamon, and turmeric. Cook for 15 minutes (you can also start this step in a separate pot while the cauliflower cooks).

Mix 1.5 cups cauliflower puree into the turkey and vegetables.

Transfer the turkey and vegetable mix to a deep casserole dish. Top with the remaining cauliflower puree. Bake for 15 minutes..

Note

You can assemble this dish in advance. To reheat, place in a cold oven, turn the heat on 375, and bake for 30 minutes.

You can replace the turkey with lean ground chicken or beef. If chopping vegetables is too challenging, use shredded carrots, shredded cabbage, frozen chopped spinach, or/and frozen broccoli florets.

SALMON WITH COLLARD GREENS AND BEANS

Serves 4

FOR THE SALMON:

1 pound wild-caught salmon fillets

1 tablespoon extra virgin olive oil

2 garlic cloves, minced

1 teaspoon fresh ginger root, finely chopped

¼ teaspoon sea salt

¼ teaspoon ground black pepper

1 tablespoon lemon juice

FOR THE VEGETABLES:

1 pound collard greens (about one large bunch), chopped

2 tablespoons extra virgin olive oil

1 medium onion, chopped

4 garlic cloves, chopped

2 tablespoons fresh ginger root, chopped

2 cups cooked white beans

½ teaspoon sea salt

½ teaspoon ground black pepper

½ teaspoon ground cumin

½ teaspoon ground coriander

4 tablespoons lemon juice

Preheat the oven to 375°F.

Season the salmon with olive oil, garlic, ginger, salt, pepper, and lemon (may be done overnight). Place on a baking tray or casserole dish. Bake for 20 minutes, until it easily flakes.

In a large pot, bring 1 quart of water to a boil. Add the collard greens, making sure they're immersed in water. Simmer for 7 minutes. Drain and set aside.

Heat the olive oil in the same pot. Saute onions, garlic, and ginger until translucent. Add the beans, salt, pepper, cumin, and coriander and cook for 5 minutes. Gently fold in the collard greens. Drizzle the lemon juice.

To serve, place vegetables on the plate. Top with salmon. Squeeze more lemon juice if desired.

Note

To chop collard greens: hold the stem with one and strip away the leaf with the other. Cut each leaf in half lengthwise. Stack the leaves and chop into ribbons.

BAKED CHICKEN FAJITA

Serves 6

3 bell peppers (any color), cut into wide slices

1 onion, yellow or red, cut into wide slices

3 large tomatoes, cut into wedges

4 garlic cloves, coarsely chopped

1 small can green chiles

1½ pounds chicken breasts or tenders, cut into strips

1 teaspoon chili powder

2 teaspoons cumin

2 teaspoons coriander

½ teaspoon sea salt

½ teaspoon ground black

pepper

1 tablespoon oregano, dried

1 tablespoon basil, dried

2 tablespoons extra virgin olive oil

Freshly squeezed lemon or lime juice (optional)

Fresh cilantro (optional)

Preheat the oven to 400°F.

Place peppers, onion, tomatoes, garlic, green chiles, and chicken strips, in a baking dish.

In a small bowl, combine the chili powder, cumin, coriander, salt, pepper, oregano, and basil. Rub the chicken and vegetables with the spice mix. Drizzle the olive oil.

Bake in the oven for 30 minutes, until the chicken is fully cooked.

To serve, top with fresh cilantro and lemon or lime juice. Serve with guacamole, fresh salsa, and beans.

Note

You can assemble this dish and bake it later. After seasoning the chicken and vegetables, cover and refrigerate. When ready to cook, place the casserole dish in a cold oven then turn the oven on.

This recipe will yield moist fajita with some juices. If you prefer it dry, spread the vegetables and chicken on a large baking sheet so the liquids dry out.

THAI CHICKEN WRAPS WITH ALMOND SAUCE

Serves 6

2 tablespoons coconut oil

4 garlic cloves, minced

1 inch cube ginger, minced

1 pound uncooked chicken breast, cut into small cubes

2 celery stalks, chopped

1 cup shredded carrots

2 cups shredded cabbage

2 cups mushrooms, sliced

2 bell peppers, any color, sliced

½ stalk lemon grass, chopped

1 tablespoon raw apple cider

¼ cup almond butter

¼ cup lemon or lime juice

¼ cup water

2 tablespoons coconut aminos (or gluten-free tamari sauce)

Lettuce leaves for wrapping

Toppings: chopped basil or cilantro, chopped raw cashews, red pepper flakes, lemon wedges

Heat the oil in a wok or large saute pan. Saute the garlic and ginger until translucent. Add the chicken and saute until no longer pink.

Add the celery, carrots, cabbage, mushroom, bell peppers, lemon grass, and vinegar. Saute for 3–5 minutes.

Make the sauce. In a small bowl, combine the almond butter, lemon juice, and coconut aminos (or tamari sauce). Set aside.

When ready to eat, top a lettuce leaf with the chicken and vegetables mix. Drizzle some of the sauce on top. Garnish with desired toppings. Squeeze with more lemon juice if you desire.

Note

If you don't have time to chop the vegetables, use shredded carrots and cabbage from the grocery store. Lemon grass can be found with the fresh herbs in the produce section. It's ok to skip it if you can't find it.

Coconut aminos is soy-free alternative to soy sauce that I recommend as part of a detox plan. If you prefer soy sauce or gluten-free tamari sauce, start with half the amount first and add more if needed because they have more sodium and a stronger flavor.

SALMON WITH MANGO RICE

Serves 4

FOR THE RICE

1 cup dry long grain or Basmati brown rice

¼ teaspoon sea salt

1 tablespoon extra virgin olive oil, divided

2 garlic cloves, minced

1-inch ginger root, minced

3 stalks celery, chopped

1 mango, chopped

1 tablespoon lemon juice

¼ cup cilantro, chopped

FOR THE SALMON

1 pound salmon fillets

2 garlic cloves, minced

1-inch ginger root, minced

1 tablespoon extra virgin olive oil

2 tablespoons lemon juice

¼ teaspoon sea salt

¼ teaspoon ground black pepper

1 bunch asparagus, washed

Preheat the oven to 375°F.

Rinse the rice with a strainer under running water. Set aside. Bring 2 cups of water to a boil in a medium pot. Stir in the rice, salt, and ½ tablespoon olive oil. Bring to a gentle simmer. Turn the heat down, cover, and cook for 20–30 minutes.

Prepare the salmon. Rub the salmon fillets with minced garlic, minced ginger, olive oil, lemon juice, salt and pepper. Place on a baking sheet, leaving space to add the asparagus later. Bake for 10 minutes.

Snap the asparagus by hand to remove about 2 inches from the bottom. Place on the salmon tray 10 minutes into cooking. If the salmon produced too much drippings, use

foil paper to make a mini tray to separate the asparagus. Cook for 10 more minutes. Cook for 10 more minutes.

When the rice is done, remove it from the pot. In the same pot, heat ½ tablespoon olive oil. Saute the garlic cloves, ginger, celery, and mango until soft. Add the rice back in, along with 1 tablespoon lemon juice and cilantro. Gently combine.

To serve, divide the rice, salmon, and asparagus among four plates.

SIRLOIN STEAK WITH BEANS AND BASIL SAUCE

Serves 4

FOR THE BASIL SAUCE

¼ cup extra virgin olive oil

3 tablespoons freshly squeezed lemon juice (about 1 lemon)

2 garlic cloves

½ teaspoon sea salt

¼ teaspoon black pepper

1 cup loosely packed fresh basil leaves

FOR THE STEAK

4 pieces of grass-fed sirloin steak, about 4-5 ounces each

Sea salt and pepper

1 teaspoon avocado oil

1 cup loosely packed fresh basil leaves

2 cups white navy beans

2 cups grape tomatoes, halved

1 cup artichoke hearts, drained and chopped

2 yellow bell peppers, chopped

Combine the olive oil, lemon juice, garlic cloves, ½ teaspoon salt, ¼ teaspoon pepper and 1 cup basil leaves in a food processor. Process until smooth. Place in a serving bowl.

Season both sides of the steak with just a few shakes of salt and pepper. Heat the avocado oil in a cast-iron skillet on medium-high. Place the steak on the skillet and cook for 7 minutes. Flip and cook for 7 more minutes for medium doneness. If you're using a food thermometer, the steak is done when it reaches and internal temperature of 140°F.

Remove the steaks from the pan and wrap tightly with aluminum foil. Let them rest for 3–4 minutes.

Roughly chop the remaining cup of basil leaves. In a medium bowl, combine with the beans, grape tomatoes, artichoke hearts, and bell peppers.

To serve, divide the beans and vegetables among four plates. Top with the steak and drizzle the basil sauce on top.

POT ROAST WITH VEGETABLES

Serves 8

FOR THE ROAST:

2 pounds top round roast

½ tablespoon sea salt

1 teaspoon black pepper

1 teaspoon allspice

½ teaspoon turmeric

1 tablespoon extra virgin olive oil

FOR THE VEGETABLES:

4 large carrots

2 turnips

4 cups portabella mushrooms

2 tomatoes on the vine

4 cups broccoli florets

2 tablespoons extra virgin olive oil

1 teaspoon sea salt

½ teaspoon garlic powder

½ teaspoon ground black pepper

½ teaspoon ground turmeric

Preheat the oven to 250°F. Combine the olive oil, salt pepper, allspice, and turmeric in a small bowl. Coat the roast with the spices mixture.

Set the roast in a large roasting pan. Add half a cup of water and put in the oven.

Meanwhile, prepare the vegetables. Cut the carrots and turnips into 3-inch thick sticks. Cut the mushrooms in half. Cut the tomatoes in quarters. Place all vegetables in a large bowl and toss with 2 tablespoons olive oil, salt, garlic, black pepper, and turmeric.

After 1.5 hours in the oven, add the vegetables to the pan, surrounding the pot roast.

Roast for another hour for medium-rare (internal temperature of 135°F), another 1.5 hours for medium (internal temperature of 145°F), and 2 hours for well-done (internal temperature of 160°F).

Note:

The total cooking time will range from 2.5 to 3.5 hours, depending on desired doneness. Checking the internal temperature is always the best method. This recipe is perfect for a weekend dinner. You can also try making it with a slow cooker during the week.

CAULIFLOWER FRIED RICE WITH SHRIMP

Serves 4

½ head cauliflower

1 pound shrimp, deveined and tail removed (if frozen, thaw according to package)

3 teaspoons coconut oil, divided

2 large eggs

2 garlic cloves, chopped

1 tablespoon peeled and chopped fresh ginger root

2 cups shredded carrots

4 cups snow peas, ends trimmed

1 ½ cups cooked brown or white rice

¼ cup coconut aminos (or 2 teaspoons soy sauce)

½ teaspoon ground turmeric

½ teaspoon ground ginger

¼ teaspoon cayenne pepper

¼ teaspoon sea salt (to taste)

2 tablespoons scallions, chopped

2 tablespoons cilantro, chopped

¼ cup chopped cashews

Snap cauliflower florets from the stem. Wash and pat dry with a paper towel. Place in a food processor and gently process until they are the size of cooked rice. You don't want a powder or mush so don't over process. This will yield about 6 cups cauliflower rice. Alternatively, chop using a large chef knife.

In a large wok or pot, heat 1 teaspoon of coconut oil. Scramble both eggs. Remove from the pot and set aside.

Heat the second teaspoon of coconut oil. Add the shrimp. Saute for 2-3 minutes until it looks pink. Don't cook it completely just yet. Remove from the pot and set aside.

Heat the third teaspoon of coconut oil. Saute the garlic and ginger for 1 minute. Add the carrots, snow peas, and cauliflower and sauté for 5-7 minutes until the vegetables soften.

Pour in the coconut aminos and season with turmeric, ginger powder, cayenne pepper, and sea salt.

Add the cooked rice, shrimp, and scrambled eggs. Toss to combine all ingredients. Continue to cook on for 5-7 minutes.

To serve, garnish with scallions, cilantro, and cashews.

Note

You may be able to find cauliflower rice in the grocery store. You can use chicken or beef strips instead of shrimp. Coconut aminos is a soy-free alternative to soy sauce that I recommend as part of a detox plan. If you prefer soy sauce or gluten-free tamari sauce, start with half the amount and add more if needed because they have more sodium and a stronger flavor.

VEGGIE LOVERS SPAGHETTI SAUCE

Serves 6

- 1 spaghetti squash
- 1 tablespoon extra virgin olive oil
- 1 onion, chopped
- 4 garlic cloves, chopped
- 1½ pounds 95% lean ground beef
- 2 zucchinis, finely chopped
- 4 cups mushroom, chopped
- 4 cups crushed fresh tomatoes (or 2 large BPA-free cans)
- ½ teaspoon sea salt
- ¼ teaspoon ground black
- pepper
- 1 teaspoon dried oregano
- 1 teaspoon dried thyme
- ½ teaspoon dried basil

Preheat the oven to 400°F. Cut spaghetti squash lengthwise in half. Remove the seeds with a spoon. Place the squash with the pulp side down on a baking tray with a rim. Add about ¼ cup water. Roast for 45 minutes or until the pulp can easily come out looking like spaghetti with a fork.

Heat the olive oil in a large saucepan. Saute the onion and garlic for 1 minute. Add the ground beef and cook for 5 minutes until no longer pink. Add the zucchini, mushrooms, crushed tomatoes, salt, pepper, oregano, thyme, and basil. Simmer for 20-30 minutes. To serve, place 1 cup spaghetti squash on your plate and top with about 1 cup of the sauce.

Note

Veggie spaghetti options have less carbs and more nutrition than traditional or gluten-free grain-based pasta. Try carrot, beet, butternut squash, potato, or sweet potato noodles for a similar carb content to spaghetti squash. Zucchini or yellow squash noodles are even lower in carbs. Go to page 79 for the full recipe.

Smoothies

All smoothies are made with protein powders so they are satisfying and help you replace meals. You can access high quality clean protein powders without artificial sweeteners or fillers through the website at www.nourzibdeh.com/shop.

If you prefer to not use protein powders, you need to make up for the protein. Add 2 to 4 tablespoons nuts or seeds like almonds, hemp, or chia. You may need an additional protein source on the side with your smoothie like a boiled egg or leftover shredded chicken.

In general, when using fresh fruit, add some ice to make the smoothie cold. If you're starting with frozen fruit, your smoothie may be a little too thick because of the ice. Add some water to dilute it.

Store any leftovers in a glass jar and drink the same or the next day. Shake right before drinking.

KALE PINEAPPLE SMOOTHIE

Serves 1

1 cup kale

1½ cup coconut water

1 cup fresh pineapple

chucks

1 tablespoon almond butter

1 scoop unflavored protein

powder (either collagen, hemp, or pea protein, about 15-20 grams protein)

Add kale leaves and coconut water to your blender. Blend for 1 minute or until the leaves are completely chopped up.

Add pineapple chucks, almond butter, and protein powder. Blend for another minute.

Note

You can use spinach or other greens instead of kale, and other fruits like apple, peaches, pears, or mango instead of pineapple.

AVOCADO SPINACH SMOOTHIE

Serves 1

1 cup spinach

½ cup parsley

1½ cup coconut water

1 cup fresh or frozen mango pieces

¼ avocado

1 scoop unflavored protein powder (either collagen, hemp, or pea protein, about 15-20 grams protein)

Blend spinach leaves, parsley, and coconut water.

When greens are chopped completely, add the mango, avocado, and protein powder. Pulse few times to combine.

Note

You can use other greens instead of spinach and other fruits like apple, orange, pear, or pineapple instead of the mango.

BANANA PEACH SMOOTHIE

Serves 1

1 cup peaches, fresh or frozen, cubed or sliced

½ medium banana

1 cup coconut milk (dairy-replacement, or almond milk)

3 tablespoon chia seeds

½ scoop unflavored protein powder (either collagen, hemp, or pea protein, about 15-20 grams protein)

Add all ingredients to your blender and blend until smooth.

Note

You can easily make this recipe with mangoes or pineapple instead of peaches.

CREAMY STRAWBERRY SMOOTHIE

Serves 1

1 cup frozen strawberries

½ medium banana

1 cup coconut milk (dairy-replacement, or almond milk)

2 tablespoons almond butter (or fresh almonds)

1 scoop unflavored protein powder (either collagen, hemp, or pea protein, about 15-20 grams protein)

Mix all ingredients in a blender and enjoy.

Note

You can use any berries like raspberries or blueberries or mixed berries instead of the strawberries. Keep in mind that berries can be a little tart.

PURPLE SMOOTHIE

Serves 1

....

1 cup packed baby spinach

1½ cups water

1 cup frozen or fresh
   blueberries

1 scoop protein powder,
   (either collagen, hemp,
   or pea protein, about 15-
   20 grams protein)

1 teaspoon coconut oil

½ inch cube fresh ginger
   root

Place spinach and water in your blender.
Blend for 1–2 minutes.

Add remaining ingredients and blend until
smooth. Drink immediately.

Note

*Coconut oil helps balance the fruit and
protein in the smoothie. Ginger has many
healthy benefits and adds an interesting
bite to the drink.*

CILANTRO CITRUS SMOOTHIE

Serves 1

1 fresh orange

1 cup coconut water

1 cup spinach

¼ cup cilantro

2 tablespoon chia seeds

1 scoop protein powder

(either collagen, hemp, or pea protein, about 15-20 grams protein)

½ cup ice

Wash the orange well. Grate the zest, about 1 teaspoon, and place in your smoothie cup. Peel the skin.

In a blender, add coconut water, spinach, and cilantro. Blend until greens are finely chopped.

Add the orange, chia seeds, protein powder, and ice. Blend or pulse until well combined.

Note

Orange zest has compounds that boost detoxification. In combination with cilantro, this smoothie is a true detox smoothie.

Small
Bites

Savory
Bites

HOMEMADE CHUNKY SALSA

Makes 3-4 cups

5 tomatoes on the vine, chopped, seeds removed and liquid drained

2 tablespoons finely chopped onion

2 garlic cloves, minced

½ green bell pepper, finely chopped

¼ cup chopped fresh cilantro

½ jalapeno pepper (or more if desired), finely chopped

1 lime, juiced (or more if desired)

¼ teaspoon sea salt

Combine all ingredients. Serve immediately or store in the fridge until ready to serve.

Note

You can add a cup of diced mango, peach, blueberries, or pineapple to make a naturally sweet salsa. You can also mix in a diced avocado. Just remember that it will brown, so only add as much avocado to the amount of salsa you plan to eat that day.

CHUNKY OR SMOOTH GUACAMOLE

Makes 2 cups

....

2 avocados

1 lemon or lime, juiced
(about 3–4 tablespoons)

½ medium onion, finely
chopped

2 garlic cloves, minced

½ teaspoon sea salt

¼ teaspoon black or
cayenne pepper,
optional for hot
guacamole

1 Roma tomatoes or
tomatoes on the vine,
diced and seeds
removed

2 tablespoons chopped
cilantro

Cut the avocadoes in half. Remove the seed.
Scoop with a spoon into a medium-size
bowl. Immediately drizzle lemon juice.

For a chunky guacamole, use two knives
to cut the avocados in opposite directions.
Make sure the avocados are coated well with
lemon juice.

For a smooth guacamole, use a fork, pestle,

or potato masher to mash the avocados.
Make sure the avocados are coated well with
lemon juice.

Add in the onion, garlic, salt, pepper, and
cumin and mix to combine. Fold in the
tomatoes and cilantro.

MIDDLE EASTERN EGGPLANT DIP (BABA GHANOUSH)

Makes 3–4 cups

4 medium eggplants

2 garlic cloves, peeled

⅓ cup tahini paste (or more, to taste)

3 tablespoon lemon juice (or more, to taste)

½ teaspoon sea salt

¼ teaspoon ground black

pepper

Olive oil for garnish

Chopped parsley for garnish

Preheat the oven to 400°F.

Wash eggplants. Using a fork or a knife, poke them all around. Place the eggplants on a baking sheet or foil paper and roast for 1 hour until soft and squishy.

Meanwhile, mince the garlic cloves in a mortar and pestle. Combine in a small bowl with tahini sauce, lemon juice, salt, and black pepper.

Allow the eggplants to cool for 15 minutes before handling them. Place them on a cutting board. Cut out the stem. Using a knife or

your hands, remove the skin. At this point, you can do one of two things. You can chop the eggplants finely with a large knife on the cutting board or you can place them in a bowl and mince them using a pestle.

Combine the chopped or minced eggplant with the tahini mixture and gently toss. Check the taste and add more salt, lemon, or tahini if you desired.

Pour into a shallow bowl or spread on a plate. Drizzle some olive oil and garnish with chopped parsley. Serve with cut-up veggies or on the side with grilled kebabs.

Note

This dish is traditionally served with pita bread and a common appetizer with grilled chicken or beef kebabs. You can enjoy it as an appetizer, snack, or side dish. Scoop this eggplant dip with cut up vegetables like carrot sticks, celery, endive lettuce, bell pepper, or cucumbers.

HUMMUS DIP

Makes 4 cups

....

4 cups cooked chickpeas

½ cup warm water

4 fresh garlic cloves

1 teaspoon sea salt (or to taste)

¼ cup tahini sauce

2 tablespoons extra virgin olive oil

1 lemon, juiced, about 4 tablespoons

Chickpeas blend better when warm. Place them in a pot with water and bring to a boil. Drain.

Place the chickpeas and ½ cup warm water in a blender. Process until creamy and smooth. Add more water if the chickpeas are still dry or too chunky.

Add the garlic cloves, salt, tahini sauce, and olive oil. Blend until smooth. Add the lemon juice and pulse few times.

Taste and add more salt, tahini or lemon if desired.

Note

There are many ways you can vary this hummus recipe:

Original: *serve seasoned with cumin, paprika, and more olive oil. Garnish with parsley.*

Roasted bell pepper: *add 1 cup of roasted red bell peppers to the blender towards the end for a chunky roasted bell pepper hummus. Add it early on with the chickpeas for a smooth roasted bell pepper hummus.*

Artichoke: *add 1 cup of artichoke hearts to the blender towards the end for a chunky artichoke hummus. Add it early on with the chickpeas for a smooth artichoke hummus.*

OLIVE TAPENADE

Makes 2.5 cups

....

¼ cup sun dried tomatoes

1 small garlic clove

1 cup black Kalamata
    olives, pitted

1 cup green olives, pitted

¼ cup capers

¼ cup fresh basil

¼ cup fresh parsley

¼ teaspoon dried oregano

¼ cup extra virgin olive oil

Place the sundried tomatoes and garlic in a food processor and pulse few times. Add olives, capers, basil, parsley, and oregano and pulse until chopped into small pieces.

Add the olive oil and pulse a few times to combine.

Note

Serve with fresh vegetables like carrots, cucumber, celery, or bell peppers, or serve on top of roasted vegetables or cooked fish, chicken, or meats.

LENTIL AND EGGPLANT BOWL

Makes 4-5 cups

1½ cup uncooked brown lentils, washed

1 large eggplant, peeled and cut into ½ inch cubes

1 garlic clove

1 tablespoon pomegranate molasses

½ lemon, juiced

1 tablespoon rice flour or potato starch

½ teaspoon sea salt

2 tablespoons extra virgin olive oil

Place the lentils and eggplant in a medium-size pot. Cover with at least 2 inches of water. Bring to a boil. Cover and simmer on low heat for 20–30 minutes until the lentils and eggplant are completely cooked. Keep checking the water as lentils absorb it very quickly and can easily burn.

Meanwhile, mince the garlic clove in a mortar and pestle. Combine with the pomegranate molasses, lemon juice, flour, and salt in a small bowl. Whisk to make sure there are no flour clumps.

Mix the pomegranate molasses mixture into the lentils and eggplant after they are cooked. Remove from the heat immediately. Drizzle with the olive oil and mix again.

Pour in a serving bowl or dip bowl. Allow it to cool to room temperature before serving.

NORI (SEAWEED) WRAPS

Makes 4 wraps

....

4 nori (seaweed) wraps

2 tablespoons hummus

2 tablespoons guacamole

**Shredded or thinly
sliced vegetables like
carrots, bell peppers,
cucumbers, spinach,**

etc.

**Optional: shredded chicken
or cooked shrimp**

Spread each nori wrap with a tablespoon
of either hummus or guacamole. Top with
shredded vegetables. If you have chicken or
shrimp, add as well.

Fold each sheet from the side to the center
to make wraps. Serve immediately.

ROASTED CHILI CHICKPEAS

Makes 3 cups

....

3 cups cooked chickpeas,   **2 tablespoons avocado oil**   **¼ teaspoon cumin**
   about 2 cans (see note)   **½ teaspoon chili powder**   **¼ teaspoon sea salt**

Place a piece of parchment paper on a baking sheet. Preheat the oven to 400°F.

Rinse the chickpeas thoroughly in water if you're using a can or carton. Place on a flat plate and pat dry with a paper towel.

Spread over a baking sheet. Drizzle with avocado oil and season with chili powder, cumin, and sea salt. Make sure all the chickpeas are coated.

Roast in the oven for 30-40 minutes. Check on them at the 30-minute mark to make sure they don't burn. Check the seasonings and add more if desired.

Turn the oven off and keep them in the oven until they completely cool for at least 2 hours or overnight. This will yield crunchy chickpeas.

Note

Choose BPA-free cans or carton. You can also cook the chickpeas from scratch. See the recipes on pages 80 and 81.

LEMON HERB CHICKPEAS

Makes 3 cups

3 cups cooked chickpeas, about 2 cans (see note)

2 tablespoons avocado oil

1 teaspoon dried thyme

½ teaspoon dried sage

¼ teaspoon sea salt

Juice of 1 lemon

Place a piece of parchment paper on a baking sheet. Preheat the oven to 400°F.

Rinse the chickpeas thoroughly in water if you're using a can or carton. Place on a flat plate and pat dry with a paper towel.

Spread over a baking sheet. Drizzle with avocado oil, and season with thyme, sage, and sea salt. Make sure all the chickpeas are coated.

Roast in the oven for 30-40 minutes. Check on them at the 30-minute mark to make sure they don't burn.

Remove from the oven and drizzle the juice of 1 lemon. Check the seasonings and add more if desired.

Turn the oven off and place the chickpea tray back in the oven. Keep them there until they completely cool for at least 2 hours or overnight. This will yield crunchy chickpeas.

Note

Choose BPA-free cans or carton. You can also cook the chickpeas from scratch. See the recipes on pages 80 and 81.

Sweet Bites

DATE CHIA MUFFINS

Makes 12 muffins

2½ cups almond flour

¾ teaspoon baking soda

½ teaspoon sea salt

2 teaspoons cinnamon

3 large eggs

1 teaspoon vanilla

2 tablespoons pure maple syrup

Zest of 1 orange

2 tablespoons melted coconut oil

½ teaspoon apple cider vinegar

⅓ cup unsweetened applesauce

½ cup chopped dates

2 tablespoons chia seeds

Preheat the oven to 375°F. Line a 12-muffin tray with muffin paper.

Combine almond flour, baking soda, salt and cinnamon in a large bowl.

In a medium bowl, whisk the eggs. Stir in the vanilla, maple syrup, orange zest, coconut oil, vinegar, and applesauce.

Mix the dry ingredients into the liquid ingredients. Fold in the chopped dates and chia seeds.

Bake for 30 minutes or until a toothpick comes out clean.

COCONUT CHOCOLATE CHIP MUFFINS

Makes 12 Muffins

1 cup coconut flour

½ teaspoon baking soda

2 tablespoons cocoa powder

4 large eggs

1 teaspoon vanilla extract

2 tablespoons maple syrup

¼ cup coconut oil, melted

1 cup coconut milk (See note below)

2 large ripe bananas, mashed

1 tablespoon apple cider vinegar

½ cup chocolate chips (optional, use dairy-free dark chocolate for dairy-free muffins)

Preheat the oven to 350°F. Line a 12-cup muffin tray with muffin paper.

Combine the coconut flour, baking soda, and cocoa powder in a small bowl. Use a fork to break any clumps.

In a large bowl, whisk the eggs. Stir in the vanilla, maple syrup, coconut oil, coconut milk, mashed banana, and apple cider vinegar.

Mix the dry ingredients into the liquid ingredients.Fold in the chocolate chips.

Spoon the batter into the muffin cups.

Bake for 30 minutes or until a toothpick comes out clean.

Note

Use coconut milk from BPA-free cans. Read the label and make sure it doesn't contain other ingredients. If the milk is clumpy, stir with a spoon to mix the water part with the solid part before adding in.

BANANA ALMOND MUFFINS

makes 12 muffins

1½ cups almond flour/meal

1½ cups brown rice flour

2 teaspoons baking powder

2 teaspoons cinnamon

4 large eggs

¼ cup coconut oil, melted

¼ cup pure maple syrup

¼ cup water

2 ripe bananas, mashed

Preheat the oven to 325°F. Line a 12-muffin tray with muffin paper.

Combine the almond flour, rice flour, baking powder, and cinnamon in a medium bowl.

Whisk the eggs, coconut oil, maple syrup, water, and mashed bananas in another bowl.

Mix the dry ingredients into the liquid ingredients.

Spoon into the muffin tray. Bake for 30 minutes until golden or a toothpick comes out clean.

ZUCCHINI BREAD

Makes 12 small slices

- 2 tablespoons melted coconut oil, divided
- 1 large zucchini
- 1 ½ cups almond flour
- ½ cup gluten-free rolled oats
- ½ cup amaranth or rice flour
- 1 teaspoon baking soda
- 1 teaspoon sea salt
- 2 teaspoons ground cinnamon
- 3 large eggs
- 1 teaspoon raw apple cider vinegar
- 2 tablespoons 100% pure maple syrup
- 1 large ripe banana, mashed

Preheat the oven to 350 degrees. Grease a small bread pan generously with 1 tablespoon of coconut oil.

Wash the zucchini and trim the ends. Place a colander on top of a bowl. Shred the zucchini into the colander. When done, pat down on the zucchini to squeeze the water out and into the bowl. Use a paper towel to collect more of the liquid. You can use this water for soups or stews.

Combine the almond flour, rolled oats, amaranth or rice flour, baking soda, salt, and cinnamon in a small bowl.

Beat the eggs with a mixer or whisk thoroughly by hand. Mix in the vinegar, maple syrup, and the remaining tablespoon of coconut oil. Mix the dry ingredients into the wet ingredient. Finally fold in the mashed banana and shredded zucchini and combine well.

Pour the batter into the bread pan. Bake for 50 minutes until a toothpick comes out clean.

Remove from the oven and let it cool for 10 minutes before removing the bread from the pan.

DATE BARS

Makes 10 bars

....

1 package pressed dates, or 16 pitted Medjool dates

⅓ cup almond butter

½ cup slivered almonds

¼ cup chia seeds

2 tablespoons cocoa powder

1 teaspoon cinnamon

½ teaspoon vanilla extract

2 scoops of unflavored Protein Powder (optional)

If using pressed dates, place all ingredients in a medium bowl. Using your hands, knead to combine and form a ball.

If using pitted dates, place all ingredients in a food processor and process until they are all sticky. Take out of the food processor and shape into a ball.

Place a 1-foot long piece of wax paper on your counter top. Place the date ball on top of it, then cover with another piece of wax paper. Flatten with a rolling pin until it reaches a thickness of 3/4 inch.

With your hand and a large knife, shape into a large rectangle or square.Cut into 10 pieces.

Wrap each bar with plastic wrap or parchment paper. Store in the fridge for a week and in the freezer for up to 3 months.

Note:

I recommend 2 scoops unflavored collagen protein powder for this recipe. Read more on collagen health benefits and products at www.nourzibdeh.com/collagen.

INDEX

Arugula and Fennel Salad with Orange Vinaigrette 109

Asian Chicken Cole Slaw 124

Avocado Salad 112

Avocado Spinach Smoothie 175

Baked Chicken Fajita 166

Banana Almond Muffins 196

Banana Peach Smoothie 176

Basic Broiled Salmon 149

Basic Salad Dressing 77

Basic Vegetable Soup 102

Beef Taco Salad 129

Beef Vegetable Stir-Fry 162

Beet and Carrot Salad 116

Black Bean Egg Bake 92

Bone Broth 75

Cauliflower Fried Rice with Shrimp 171

Chicken and Greens over Sweet Potatoes 163

Chicken Stock with Chicken Meat 72

Chicken Stock (without chicken meat) 73

Chicken with herbed tomatoes and mushrooms 145

Chickpea Mango Fusion Salad 111

Chopped Kale salad with Almond Vinaigrette 108

Chunky Brown Lentil Soup 104

Chunky or Smooth Guacamole 185

Cilantro Citrus Smoothie 179

Coconut Chicken Nuggets with Spicy Honey Mustard Sauce 148

Coconut Chocolate Chip Muffins 195

Creamy Red Potato Salad 157

Creamy Strawberry Smoothie 177

Curried Butternut Squash Soup 105

Date Bars 198

Date Chia Muffins 194

Detox Cauliflower Salad 110

Detox Sheppard's Pie 164

Dry Beans in the Slow Cooker 81

Dry Beans on the Stovetop 80

Egg Avocado Salad 91

Eggplant and Zucchini Ratatouille 132

Everyday Baked Potato or Sweet Potato 85

Everyday Lentils 82

Everyday Oatmeal 95

Everyday Quinoa 83

Everyday Rice 84

Everyday Vegetable Omelet 88

Five Herb Chicken 144

Grilled Chicken Kebabs 146

Grilled Scallop Citrus Salad 125

Grilled Zucchini 141

Hard-Boiled Eggs 76

Hearty Chicken Vegetable Stew 118

Herb Red Potatoes 158

Homemade Chunky Salsa 184

Hummus Dip 187

Kale Pineapple Smoothie 174

Lemon Garlic Shrimp 152

Lemon Herb Chickpeas 192

Lentil and Eggplant Bowl 189

Mashed Cauliflower 136

Middle Eastern Eggplant Dip (Baba Ghanoush) 186

Middle Eastern Lamb Stew with Green beans 121

Middle Eastern Parsley Salad with Tahini Dressing 114

Middle Eastern Pureed Red Lentil Soup 103

Mixed Vegetable Frittata 90

Muesli 96

Nori (Seaweed) Wraps 190

Nutty Fruit Breakfast 94

Olive Tapenade 188

Pan-Seared Scallops 151

Peach and Black Bean Salad 113

Pecan Crusted Flounder 153

Poached Eggs 89

Pomegranate Tuna Salad 127

Pot Roast with Vegetables 170

Purple Smoothie 178

Quinoa Vegetable Pilaf 159

Roasted Asparagus 139

Roasted Brussels Sprouts 135

Roasted Chili Chickpeas 191

Roasted Eggplant Salad 115

Roasted Peppers and Mushrooms 133

Roasted Spaghetti Squash 156

Roasted Turmeric Cauliflower 140

Salmon with Collard Greens and Beans 165

Salmon with Mango Rice 168

Sautéed Collard Greens 137

Sautéed Colorful Cabbage 134

Shredded Chicken Breast 74

Shrimp Detox Salad 128

Sirloin Steak with Beans and Basil sauce 169

Steamed Vegetables 78

Sweet Potato Pancakes 97

Tex-Mex Chicken Soup 119

Thai Chicken Wraps with Almond Sauce 167

Tomato Clam Chowder 106

Tomato Olive Baked Cod 154

Tuna Avocado Salad 126

urkey chili 120

Vegetable Stuffed Portobello Mushroom 138

Veggie Lovers Spaghetti Sauce 172

Whole Chia Seed Pudding 93

Yellow Chicken with Avocado Dressing 147

Zesty Herbed Salmon 150

Zucchini Bread 197

Zucchini Noodles 79

CPSIA information can be obtained
at www.ICGtesting.com
Printed in the USA
BVHW02s1729100518
515777BV00009BA/48/P